PASSIVE SMOKE:
The EPA's Betrayal of Science and Policy

WITHDRAWN

Gio B. Gori

John C. Luik

The Fraser Institute

Vancouver British Columbia Canada 1999

VERMONT
COLLEGE

LIBRARY
MONTPELIER, VERMONT

PASSIVE SMOKE:
The EPA's Betrayal of Science and Policy

Gio B. Gori

John C. Luik

[Besides the outright fraud of deliberate plagiarism, fabrication, falsification, and misrepresentation of data, the definition of scientific misconduct should include] "the scientific counterparts of what lawyers call 'sharp practices': ... incomplete citation of previously published work; bias in peer review of ... manuscripts; or skewed selection of data to hide or disguise observations that do not fit the author's conclusions (although in some circumstances the latter could be a more serious offense). Such practices are far more widespread than the 'hard core' fraud ... [but], because of the moral climate they help to create, these ethical deviations should be treated with equal seriousness."

> Teich AH, Frankel MS. *Good science and responsible scientists. Meeting the challenge of fraud and misconduct in science.* American Association for the Advancement of Science. Washington, DC. 1992, p. 4.

Printed and bound in Canada.

Canadian Cataloguing in Publication Data

Gori, Gio B.
Passive Smoke: The EPA's Betrayal of Science and Policy

Includes bibliographical references.
ISBN 0-88975-196-X

1. United States. Environmental Protection Agency. 2. Passive smoking—Health aspects—Research—Evaluation. 3. Science—Moral and ethical aspects—United States. I. Luik, John. II. Fraser Institute (Vancouver, B.C.). III. Title.

HV5748.G67 1999   363.4   C99-910188-9

Contents

About the Authors

GIO BATTA GORI is a long time defender of sound science as a foundation of fair public policy in health and safety; he has broad interests and experience in toxicology, epidemiology, nutrition, smoking and health, and environmental issues. He has lectured widely in North America, Europe, and many countries, appeared at several hearings in the U.S. Congress and foreign governments, and has advised corporations internationally. Born in Friuli, Italy, he obtained a doctorate in biology after an education in the classics. In the United States he first worked with the late Jonas Salk, followed by academic and industrial experiences. During a distinguished tenure at the National Cancer Institute he was deputy director of the Division of Cancer Cause and Prevention, and directed the Smoking and Health Program and the Diet and Cancer Program. He was recognized with the U.S. Public Health Service Superior Service Award for his achievements in smoking and health. Later he organized and directed the Franklin Institute Policy Analysis Center, followed by his own Health Policy Center, a study and advisory group in health policy and regulation. He publishes extensively on scientific and policy matters.

JOHN C. LUIK has taught philosophy and management studies at a number of universities, has been Senior Associate of the Niagara Institute with responsibility for its work in public policy and leadership and organizational change, and has worked as a consultant for governmental institutions, professional organizations and corporations in the United States, Europe, Asia, Africa, the Middle East and Latin America.

He was educated on a Rhodes Scholarship at the University of Oxford where he obtained the BA, MA and D.Phil. degrees. His academic interests include public policy, particularly the use of science in policy and the question of government intervention to change risky behaviours, the ethics of advertising and business, and philosophy. He is a frequent media commentator and conference speaker and the author of numerous articles and several books. His most recent publications include: "The Assault on Pleasure: Health Promotion and Engineering the Human Soul", "Pandora's Box: The Dangers of Corrupted Science for Democratic Public Policy", *Smokescreen: Passive Smoking and Public Policy*, "I Can't Help Myself: Addiction as Ideology", *Advertising and Markets*, "Humanism", and "The Problem of Permission for Pleasure in a Democratic Society".

Publisher's Preface

Does second-hand smoke result in thousands of deaths every year in the U.S. and Canada? If you have been listening to health advocates in the media, the answer is an emphatic yes. This premature conclusion is largely based on a 1993 report by the U.S. Environmental Protection Agency (EPA) which concluded that second-hand cigarette smoke caused around 3,000 deaths per year among nonsmokers. This report was used by anti-tobacco activists to secure bans (full or partial) on indoor smoking in the U.S. and Canada.

This kind of health warning is persuasive for two reasons. One, the EPA is a government agency that is generally considered credible. Second, a significant number of people think smoking is unhealthy. Due to the latter reason in particular, people are inclined to believe news reports suggesting that second-hand smoke is harmful and causes death.

In a recent ruling, Judge William Osteen of the Middle District of North Carolina invalidated the EPA study linking exposure to second-hand smoke, also known as environmental tobacco smoke (ETS), to 3,000 cancer deaths each year. Judge Osteen concluded that the researchers at the EPA frequently shifted theories and cherry-picked data in order to reach a preconceived conclusion.

The unfortunate reality is that this is not a unique circumstance. Many products today are being deemed harmful without the benefit of careful scientific research. Recent examples of products which are said to be harmful to health include, cell phones, hot dogs, chlorinated drinking water, red meat, and second-hand smoke. In other words, products are being banned based on "junk science." As Professor Cornelia J. Baines, notes: "Junk science, including the inappropriate application of untested hypotheses to important health issues is a menace to society and to science."

Steven Milloy in his book *Science Without Sense: The Risky Business of Public Health Research* lays out some critical success factors for junk science to triumph over careful scientific research. This list includes: the selection of an unprovable risk, an ubiquitous risk, a risk which is intuitive to the public, a risk which can not be defended easily, a risk that is involuntary, a risk which the public will be willing to reduce if there is no major personal sacrifice, and finally pick a risk that is novel.

As we will see each of these principles are at work in many of the examples that follow.

As Professors Mark Neal and Christie Davies point out:

> A good example of the new and increasingly powerful breed of health zealots came in the form of the former Canadian Minister of Health, M Marc Lalonde. His view on health matters was that the state regulators should not wait for solid evidence of risk before imposing increased regulations, or bans. This approach to public welfare matters became known as the Lalonde Doctrine, which stated even when evidence was uncertain and ambiguous health message to the public should be "loud, clear and unequivocal." Fired up with this agenda the Canadian authorities forced the cigarette manufacturers to inscribe "Passive Smoking Causes Cancer" on their packets even though there was no persuasive evidence that it did.

Due in part to the extensive use of the Lalonde Doctrine by health advocates, the challenge, today, is to provide protection for the public against environmental and health hazards without unduly stifling the ability of people to enjoy the benefits of new technologies and products. This task, however, is proving to be enormously difficult in the debate about ETS as well as others.

For example, the Food and Drug Administration (FDA) started to raise questions about the safety of silicone breast implants and finally in 1992 issued a ban. The basis for the ban was the fact that the manufacturers had not adequately demonstrated their safety. The "scientific" basis for the ban was the belief that silicone adversely affects the auto-immune system. The ban by the FDA induced a flurry of lawsuits against the manufacturers of silicone breast implants in the U.S. and Canada. These lawsuits were often successful with billion dollar settlements. While these lawsuits were being settled, hard research evidence began to surface. The evidence seems to suggest that silicone was relatively safe. As Marcia Angell has noted:

> At the time of the ban on breast implants, David Kessler acknowledged that there was no evidence that breast implants caused connective tissue disease. He simply felt he could not wait for the evidence to be assembled before banning them. For their part, the courts had long since decided that implants caused connective tissue disease. Now, years later, the evidence is beginning to emerge. We are beginning to see that any connection

between implants and connective tissue disease is likely to be very weak at most, since several good studies have failed to detect it. Given the absence of scientific evidence at the time, why were the courts so sure of their conclusions?

In yet another example, when scientists discovered that large doses of ethylene dibromide (EDB) caused cancer in rodents, governments banned the chemical from use as a fumigant to keep insects and molds off stored grains. Yet the average amount of EDB ingested by people with normal diets was a thousand times less risky than the natural carcinogens in two slices of bread. Moreover, EDB is the safest known way to combat molds, which produce some of the most potent carcinogens in nature. This kind of response by regulators ensures the regulation of trivial and perceived risks as opposed to real material risks.

Not every disease and not all threats to human health merit equal public concern. Although cancer kills fewer Canadians and Americans than heart disease, cancer receives more attention from the public health community because we feel that an external force causes it. Therefore, we hope, by identifying the causes (environmental risks) we can reduce its death toll.

In response to our fears and in the hopes of identifying and controlling causes, risk assessment has emerged as a discipline designed to estimate health risks from various sources and attempt to reduce them. There are two kinds of risk assessment. Technological risk assessment focuses on predicting the safety of dams, nuclear power plants, airplanes and etc. We seldom hear about them except when there is an accident.

Health risk assessment, on the other hand, is commonly in the news. Every time a new chemical is introduced into a consumer product, some health policy expert will provide so-called evidence to suggest that it is carcinogenic. On its heels, someone will provide an estimate of the health risk.

Increasingly, regulation of chemicals is being governed by political responses to public fear and hysteria rather than careful, objective scientific evaluations of the actual risks and benefits posed by environmental hazards including chemicals and their use. For example, there are trace amounts of natural carcinogens (toxins) all around us. They do not, however, pose a health risk. In conducting rodent tests to regulate chemicals many toxicology tests use what is known as maximum tolerated doses rather than trace amounts. Straight-line extrapolations from these rodent studies are then applied to humans. Using these studies to set thresholds for chemical toxins in humans exaggerates the risk.

A majority of Canadians and Americans get a significant amount of information about health risks from the media. The debate about global warming and whether or not Canada and the U.S. should sign a treaty to reduce greenhouse gas emissions provides another good example of how the reliance on the media to inform you about health risks can give you a rather distorted picture of the real magnitude of the risk.

There is debate going on among scientists about whether fossil fuel emissions cause global warming. Some scientists conclude that they do. In light of some evidence to the contrary, many other respected scientists are rather skeptical. In short, there is no consensus in the scientific community on whether human usage of fossil fuels is the main cause of global warming, if indeed global warming is occurring. If one reads the paper or watches television, you would be led to believe that there is a scientific consensus.

The manner in which the EPA handled the evidence or lack thereof with respect to ETS is indicative of the misuse of the scientific method and the media reporting of the issue. If people begin to distrust scientific evidence, then effective and efficient public policy making is in jeopardy. Moreover, citizens will begin to distrust the institutions that make public policy. The misuse of science could have disastrous consequences. In democracies, the objective of public policy should be to minimize harm to citizens by rational public discourse based on scientific and documented evidence.

The adherence to standards of rationality is critical. Evidence must be marshaled to support a hypothesis. Depending on the evidence, public policies should be formulated to address the problem. Moreover, the proposed solutions must not only have the promise of being effective but also must be evaluated to make sure that they are effective.

Another important issue that policy makers should pay attention to is the role of risk management. Risk management can be defined as the application of policies and procedures to the task of analyzing, evaluating, controlling, and communicating about risk. In order to ensure the integrity of science and its collorary risk assessment, policy makers must not exaggerate harm. Moreover, they must also provide risk assessment in the context of other risks so those individuals can compare risks that they face. Further, it is incumbent upon regulators to explain to the public the inexact nature of risk assessment and the complexities inherent in such assessments.

Clearly, for a democracy to work and for bureaucratic and political accountability to be meaningful, the public deserves to be informed about the realties of risk management. In spite of the accumulating research evidence, government agencies in Canada and the U.S. continue to regulate less risky activities based on bad science with little or no consideration for the actual costs. The cost of regulatory compliance for the Canadian economy was $83 billion in 1995-96. In the U.S., the cost of regulatory compliance was $688 billion in 1997. Science-based decision-making and comparative risk assessment are relegated to the back burner with adverse consequences for economic growth.

In this book, Dr. Gio Batta Gori of the Health Policy Center in Bethesda, Maryland, and Dr. John Luik critically examine the science on which ETS studies are based. They also discuss and critique the so-called scientific method used by the EPA in its 1993 study on ETS. In doing so, the authors go on to discuss the decision rendered by Judge Osteen. In their conclusion, the authors argue that if the science underpinning public policy is not sound, the public's distrust of regulatory decisions in every aspect of our lives will be amplified with disastrous consequences.

The Fraser Institute is publishing this book as part of its regulatory studies program. In light of the fact that regulation imposes a heavy cost on the economy and consequently retards productivity growth and our standard of living, it is critical governments pay more attention to the regulatory decisions.

The latest Institute publications on regulatory matters include:

- Regulatory Overkill: The Cost of Regulation in Canada (1996)

- Federal Regulatory Reform: Rhetoric or Reality? (1997)

- Canadian Content Regulations: The Intrusive State At Work (1998)

- The Cost of Regulation in Canada 1998 Edition (1998)

- Overweening Ambition: Assessing the CRTC's Plans to Regulate the Internet (1998)

- Bank Mergers: The Rational Consolidation of Banking in Canada (1998)

- Vehicle Emissions Testing: Air Care, Drive Clean, and Potential of Inspection and Maintenance Programs in Canada (1998)

- The Economics of Minimum Wage Laws (1998)

The authors of this study, Dr. Gio Batta Gori and Dr. John Luik have independently produced this research. Therefore, while The Fraser Institute is happy to publish their research, the views expressed may not conform to those of the Members and the Trustees of the Fraser Institute.

References

Ames, Bruce and Lois Swirsky Gold. "The Causes and Prevention of Cancer: The Role of Environment," In Ronald Bailey ed., *The True State of the Planet*, New York: The Free Press, 1995, pp. 141-177.

Angell, Marcia. *Science on Trial – The Clash of Medical Evidence and the Law in the Breast Implant Case*, New York: W.W. Norton and Company, 1996.

Baines, Cornelia. "Junk science must be stopped," *The Financial Post*, November 23, 1998, p. C5.

Gori, Gio Batta. "Science, Policy, and Ethics: The Case of Environmental Tobacco Smoke", Journal of Clinical Epidemiology, Vol. 47, No. 4, 1994, pp. 325-334.

Graham, John and Jonathan Baert Weiner. eds., *Risk vs. Risk: Tradeoffs in Protecting Health and the Environment*, Cambridge, Massachusetts: Harvard University Press, 1995.

Jones, Laura. ed., *Global Warming: The Science and the Politics*, Vancouver: The Fraser Institute, 1997.

Luik, John. "Pandora's Box: The Dangers of Politically Corrupted Science for Democratic Public Policy," *Bostonia*, Winter 93-94, pp. 50-60.

Luik, John. "Smokescreen 'Passive Smoking' and Public Policy," *Current Issues*, Australia: Institute of Public Affairs, 1996.

Meier, Barry. "Judge Voids Study Linking Cancer to Secondhand Smoke," *New York Times*, July 20, 1998, p. A14.

Mihlar, Fazil. "Regulatory Overkill: The Cost of Regulation in Canada," *Critical Issues Bulletin*, Vancouver: The Fraser Institute, 1996.

Mihlar, Fazil. "Federal Regulatory Reform: Rhetoric or Reality?" *Public Policy Source*, Vancouver: The Fraser Institute, 1997.

Mihlar, Fazil. "The Cost of Regulation in Canada (1998 Edition)," *Public Policy Source*, Vancouver: The Fraser Institute, 1998.

Milloy, Steven. *Science Without Sense: The Risky Business of Public Health Research*, Washington, D.C.: The Cato Institute, 1995.

Morrison, Kate. "Energy and the Environment: A Report on the Vancouver Sun," *On Balance*, Vol. 11, No. 4, April, 1998.

Neal, Mark and Christie Davies. *The Corporation Under Siege: Exposing the Devises Used by Activists and Regulators in the Non-risk Society*, London: The Social Affairs Unit, 1998.

Torrance, Kelly. "Risky News," *The Fraser Forum*, Vancouver: The Fraser Institute, October, 1998, pp. 13-16.

Wildavsky, Aaron. "Regulation of Carcinogens: Are Animal Tests a Sound Foundation?" *The Independent Review* Vol. 1, No. 1, Spring, 1996.

Foreword

Public opinion makers are still reeling from a July 17, 1998 Federal Court decision that nullified the 1992 report of the US Environmental Protection Agency on environmental tobacco smoke (ETS)—the Court having determined that the Agency acted illegally and misrepresented claims that ETS causes 3060 lung cancer cases a year in the US alone. For 20 years these opinion makers have relied on the EPA's and other previous reports to proclaim that ETS is a major health menace—thus debasing smokers to the moral equivalent of baby killers, and motivating countless legal actions worth billions of dollars in punitive damages. What could be the matter with this Federal Court? Have they not followed the news all these years?

Predictably, some in the game are trying to wave the Court's action away by insinuating that this is a North Carolina Court—tobacco country—without taking time to find that Judge William Osteen, who decided against the EPA, is the same judge who previously dealt the tobacco industry a major defeat by finding that nicotine is a drug and giving the Food and Drug Administration the authority to regulate tobacco. More likely, though, the same opinion makers may be reluctant to even read Judge Osteen's decision because of a nagging fear of finding it wholly convincing. In fact it is both convincing, and written in a language accessible to anyone with an open mind who takes the time to be be somewhat acquainted with the legalities and the science involved.

The legalities are simple. The EPA claims to have acted under the authority of the Radon Research Act, but it willfully frustrated the intent of the Act and disingenuously tried to mislead the Court into believing otherwise. The EPA's science simply does not exist. As the Court found, the EPA never asked whether ETS is or is not a risk for lung cancer, but began with the unsupported affirmation that it is and then set out to bolster its claim by whatever means.

This meant that the Agency cherry-picked suitable reports, graded their credibility by their accordance with its own claims, haughtily disregarded obvious explanations for opposite conclusions, fiddled with statistical procedure to feign nonexisting precision, and abused its public trust by spinning deceptive public messages with far reaching and ominous regulatory, social, and cultural consequences. It cannot be said that the EPA acted in good faith and was merely technically incompetent or careless to the point of dereliction of duty, for its interactions with the Court show a conceited attempt at deception. This picture emerges clearly from Judge Osteen's decision, written in a restrained language that shows his deep distaste of the EPA's misdeeds. In the latest show of arrogance, the EPA filed an appeal to the Court's decision, arguing not so much on the substance of the ruling but rather that it is irrelevant, advancing the evasive claim that Court has no jurisdiction over the Agency.

Our intent in writing this book is to expand on the information accessory to Judge Osteen's decision and not available to most readers. We also discuss the philosophical and scientific background that is essential for interpreting the evidence at hand, and for the full appreciation of how corrupt the EPA's misuse of science is. At the same time we know that killing the messenger is a much abused pastime, and that some will dismiss our analysis because both of us are sometime consultants to the tobacco industry.

Stated many times, our position is that smoking is unfortunate and risky. The evidence tells us the health risks of smoking are confined to smokers. The risks are well known to smokers, who may or may not have balanced those risks against the rewards of smoking—rewards that are pleasurable, and that entrain smokers in a habit they find of value in the normal expression of their lives. We believe smokers should continue to be made aware of their risks, but ultimately the decision not to smoke is personal and should not be enforced by the state, especially not on the authority of false pretexts. As for environmental smoke, private arrangements guided by taste, courtesy, and good sense should be enough.

Here, the points we discuss happen to be favorable to the tobacco industry, but in reality we are arguing for the higher truths that government agencies in free societies have the sacred duty to uphold in shaping public policy. Much has been made of tobacco industry lies, yet here we have not a private commercial interest but the EPA, a public agency chartered and funded to provide truthful information and factually based norms, caught red-handed in a conspiracy of public disinformation and in an attempt to deceive the Court. We think something can be done, must be done, lest we surrender to a grasping bureaucracy and to merit King Lear's reproach: "... get thee glass eyes, and, like a scurvy politician, seem to see the things thou dost not" (King Lear, 4,6).

Gio B. Gori
John C. Luik

Bethesda, Maryland. January 1999

Glossary

EPA   - United States Environmental Protection Agency

ETS   - Environmental tobacco smoke (second-hand smoke, passive smoke)

IAQC   - Indoor Air Quality / Total Human Exposure Committee of the EPA

IARC   - International Agency for Research on Cancer

MS   - Mainstream smoke (inhaled by smokers)

NRC   - National Research Council

OSHA - United States Occupational Health and Safety Administration

RR   - Relative risk

RSP   - Respirable suspended particles in smoke

SAB   - Science Advisory Board of the EPA

SS   - Side-stream smoke (coming from the smoldering cigarette)

TLV   - Threshold Limit Value (permitted occupational exposure)

Summary

Federal Judge William L. Osteen, of the US District Court for the Middle District Division of North Carolina, found reason to nullify the US Environmental Protection Agency (EPA) report of 1992, which claimed there is sufficient evidence to classify passive smoke (second-hand smoke, passive smoke, environmental tobacco smoke or ETS) as a Group A human carcinogen, and specifically as a cause of lung cancer. Here we summarize the high points that led to the Court's decision.

- It is an axiom that science is not interested in propositions that can not be tested. Unfortunately, epidemiologic studies of ETS and lung cancer do not qualify as science because they cannot test the hypothesis that ETS causes lung cancer with the rigor required by science. They provide measurements of little credibility, do not account for the bias that favors publications pointing to risk, do not account for the bias of smokers who incorrectly claim to be non-smokers or never smokers, nor for other lung cancer risk factors that may offer alternative explanation of causality. As pointed out by Judge Osteen, the combination of deficient studies and the EPA's slanted interpretation have resulted in conjectures devoid of scientific content and justification.

- The Court noted that the EPA switched to opposing arguments in different chapters, choosing whatever was momentarily expedient. For instance, at times the EPA maintains that the mainstream smoke that smokers inhale is comparable to ETS and at other times that they are different, whichever suits the moment.

- The EPA ignored that all studies reviewed include assumptions that are grossly unrealistic. The literature reports dozens of risk factors for lung cancer that may confound the results of ETS studies unless accounted for, yet the EPA ignored most of them under the convenient but absurd affirmation that they are immaterial. Such an assumption might allow the practical conduct of studies that are otherwise impossible, but hardly reflects a complex reality. The EPA simply assumes that ETS studies have accounted for potential confounders, when in reality they have not.

- The EPA dealt arbitrarily with the crucial influence of bias, especially publication and misclassification bias. In regard to the latter, it managed to trivialize that virtually all studies have not accounted for the many smokers who deceptively state to be non-smokers or never-smokers—a bias that inevitably generates a false impression of ETS risk. The Agency did so by presuming to invent low rates of misclassification based on arbitrary assumptions and ad hoc procedures.

- The EPA often distinguished better from poorer studies, but failed to describe its evaluation criteria or how they might have been applied. The EPA failed to note that virtually all studies evaluated are severely deficient, and failed to make it clear that a judgment of study quality could only range from bad to worse rather than from good to better.

- The EPA did not address broad questions about the validity of consolidating data from different studies by the meta-analysis procedure. The EPA's use of the procedure is illegitimate because the studies analyzed are a heterogeneous collection and do not justify meta-analysis summations.

- The EPA transgressed by deviating from its standard operating procedures and by adopting substandard levels of statistical significance, in order to give a false impression of robustness to its preconceived claim that ETS causes lung cancer.

- The EPA neither stated nor used standard criteria for inferring causality. The Court noted the EPA adopted whatever criteria were expedient to force its preconceived conclusion of risk, and did not try to determine whether ETS is or is not a risk for lung cancer, but started from the preconceived claim that it is and went out to prove that claim by whatever means imaginable.

- The EPA claimed to follow a "weight of evidence" approach but in reality it focused routinely on selective references and methods, reaching conclusions by cherry-picking studies said to be of the highest quality on the basis of unstated criteria and unqualified assertions.

- The EPA failed to recognize that a "weight of evidence" evaluation is expected to observe standard rules of logic that may reduce any given proposition to absurdity. For instance, it is apparent that the smokers of a few cigarettes per day likely experience no appreciable risk elevation, and therefore it would be absurd to attribute measurable effects to ETS exposures and doses that are equivalent to smoking what could be less than one cigarette a year.

- The Court found that the EPA disregarded a statutory requirement for an advisory committee broadly representative of the interests concerned, and instead used an advisory group with members mostly deferential to the Agency. Because the EPA's risk assessment was demonstrably corrupt, the Court found that a legitimate statutory committee would have caused the Agency to come to a different conclusion about ETS.

- The Court determined that the EPA had knowingly, willfully, and aggressively disseminated false information with far reaching regulatory implications in the US and worldwide.

- On account of the above, the Court ordered a summary judgment against the EPA and nullified the Agency's ETS risk assessment.

Chapter One

A Brief History of the Crusade Against Environmental Tobacco Smoke

Activism against tobacco got into high gear with the 1964 Surgeon General's report, but it was not until the Surgeon General's reports of 1972 and 1975 that the issue of passive smoking began to raise initial speculations about the possible consequences of exposure to second-hand smoke (USSG 1972, 1975). Coincidentally, the zeal and the impatience of the anti-smoking crusaders escalated in the late 70's, when it became clear that novel arguments were needed to embarrass and force the hand of smokers who were skeptical of anti-smoking messages.

Indeed, the right of individuals to smoke had been a major frustration in the campaign against tobacco, whose strategists came to realize that this right could be restricted forcibly only if it could be shown that passive exposure to environmental tobacco smoke (ETS) represents an involuntary risk to non-smokers. Thus, a major effort in this direction began with a call-to-arms in the 1979 Surgeon General's report on smoking (USSG, 1979), followed by substantial offers of research funds from agencies under the Surgeon General and the Public Health Service, and from allied interests of the American Cancer Society, The American Lung Association, the American Heart Association, and other advocacy groups.

These efforts resulted in several published reports that in 1986 became the focus of two synchronous and apparently concerted summary reviews: one by the National Academy of Science—sponsored by the Environmental Protection Agency—and the other by the Surgeon General (NAS, 1986; USSG, 1986). A third review was conducted in the same year by the International Agency for Research on Cancer (IARC), an arm of the World Health Organization heavily dependent on funding from US agencies (IARC, 1986). Not surprisingly, both US reviews came to the parallel claims that ETS increases the risk of lung cancer by some 30 percent. The IARC review, on the other hand, did not produce estimates of risk, instead concluding that available studies " ... had to contend with substantial difficulties in determination of passive expo-sure to tobacco smoke and to other possible risk factors. The resulting errors could arguably have artefactually depressed or raised estimates of risk, and, as a consequence, each is compatible either with an increase or with an absence of risk" (IARC, 1986, p. 308).

The reports of National Academy of Sciences and of the Surgeon General emboldened the anti-smoking coalitions but lacked regulatory authority, a deficiency that required engaging official agencies with the power to impose the normative restrictions that anti-smokers sought. The first remedy came as a lawsuit by a group known as Action for Smoking and health (ASH) against the U.S. Occupational Safety and Health Administration (OSHA), with the intent of forcing workplace bans on smoking. Legal action was deemed necessary because OSHA rightly saw ETS as an insignificant issue. The Agency feared that if ETS were to be regulated, then virtually all other OSHA-approved work-place exposures would have to be reduced drastically to the immaterial levels of ETS, likely bringing workplace activities in the US to a virtual standstill.

It was not until 1994 that OSHA initiated halfhearted action on a proposed rule to restrict smoking in workplaces, but to this day no regulation has been issued (USOSHA, 1994). However, in the late 80's the EPA proved much less reluctant even though it had no explicit legislative mandate that would allow direct regulation of ETS. Still, the EPA foresaw an opportunity to expand its reach by influencing regula-tion of ETS indirectly, using its authority to encourage and justify regulatory action at state and local levels.

In June 1989, a public notice issued by the Agency stated categori-cally that ETS "... is a known cause of lung cancer ...", but without providing the Agency's analysis of published data (USEPA, 1989). This fateful notice established a precedent that the Agency could not possibly repudiate without losing prestige, and also one that compelled the Agency to conduct its own analysis of the still accumulating data, in order to defend its self-attributed environmental prominence. The Agency was also pressured to conduct its own ETS risk assessment, as documented by internal EPA memos urging the acceleration of the Agency's risk assessment process because local, state, and federal agency projects were waiting for an official statement of risk—a state-ment that would allow local legislators to ban smoking in public places, restaurants, and workplaces (Rosenberg, 1991).

The context of these events explains quite well why the EPA's ETS risk assessment picked up steam around 1989 with the *a priori* (i.e. preconceived) affirmation that ETS causes lung cancer in non-smokers, rather than with the sound scientific approach of asking *whether or not* it might qualify as a cause (USEPA, 1992c, p.5-2). Still, the EPA's one sided approach could have been forgiven if the evidence and its analysis could sustain the Agency's preconceived notion, but in fact neither the evidence nor the analysis justifies the claim, and both make the Agency's position all the more egregious.

This is not unusual behavior at the EPA, an agency with a standing tradition of exceeding its authority by misinterpreting science under the political protection of numerous professional activist groups that lobby legislators and the media on its behalf. The problem is and was so obvious that around the same time it was conducting the ETS assessment, the EPA itself was compelled to ask a blue ribbon panel to inquire about the state of science at the Agency—a panel that ended up criticizing in detail how "junk science" was used by the Agency to prop its own policy agenda (USEPA, 1992e).

The EPA's tradition of misusing science is shared by others behind the passive smoke crusade. When pressed, anti-smoking zealots even admit to dealing in "junk science" but justify this intellectual scam by declaring that insisting on science is naive because "the relationship of epidemiologic and toxicologic data regarding the risk of passive smoking to regulatory action is best understood as a complex, dialectical and social process." With this reasoning, anti-smokers argue that science is immaterial and that forcible control is justified simply because society fears ETS exposure, and therefore "[i]n the context of a deeply risk-averse society ... how conclusive [do] the data need to be?" (Brandt, 1998, p.170). On its face the argument is an insult to intellectual honesty, a flight from reason and objectivity, an astonishing statement with ominous societal implications, where corrupt science is first used to establish and to amplify public anxieties about alleged risks—anxieties that are then called upon to justify the corruption of science. It is the post modernist assertion that perception is reality, the totalitarian argument of oppression that has led to so much injustice, the same argument of self-serving bigotry that burnt witches at the stake.

To this day, the EPA maintains it does not have a direct regulatory interest in ETS. The Court noted that this claim is at least disingenuous, because the EPA report on ETS has been used uncritically in the US and worldwide to enact far reaching regulations that ostracize smokers. To this day, it is invoked to justify legions of politically correct social police who pit non-smokers against smokers, wives against husbands, and children against parents in a most invidious campaign of coercive social engineering.

The EPA report and methods have become the gold standard around which later reports have been modeled with equally misleading outcomes, notably those by the California Environmental Protection Agency, by the National Health and Medical Research Council of Australia, and by the Scientific Committee on Tobacco and Health of the UK (CEPA, 1997; NHMRC, 1998; SCOTH, 1998).

At a recent hearing, the US National Toxicology Program (NTP) accepted at face value the EPA report on ETS and its twin from California, as the basis for listing ETS as a known human carcinogen in the Annual Report on Carcinogens destined to reach Congress—an action of predictable regulatory consequences (NTP, 1998). The political nature of NTP's action and its lack of scientific guidance become obvious when, during the same hearing, the NTP also failed to list diesel exhaust fumes as a known human carcinogen. It did so even though the epidemiologic and laboratory evidence for diesel exhaust—poor as it is— is relatively much stronger than the hopelessly equivocal reports on ETS.

One does not need to be a scientist to ascertain the lack of science in the ETS saga, for the evidence is as manifest as it was to Judge Osteen in his decision. In fact, there is reason to believe the EPA itself may now be conceding indirectly the absence of science, given it has filed an appeal brief that is based little on the substance of the Osteen decision which it asserts it does not matter, and where it avoids the issue by claiming that the Court has no jurisdiction over the Agency (USEPA, 1998). Still, before examining that decision in detail, it will be useful to get acquainted with the language of science and especially of epidemiology, and then to examine the data available to the EPA at the end of 1992, when its ETS report was being completed.

Chapter Two

Terms of Scientific Reference

Judge Osteen's decision to vacate the 1992 EPA report on ETS is best analyzed on scientific grounds, first by examining the claimed scientific validity of the EPA report, and then by dissecting the Court's assessment of the EPA's claims. In turn, the core of a scientific evaluation is to examine published reports for their adherence to scientific methods, which require ETS studies to have excluded other known causes of lung cancer that may corrupt the results, to have accounted for several biases that inevitably crop up, and to have obtained sufficiently accurate measurements.

An initial word of caution is necessary because today the labels "science" and "scientific" are applied wantonly and often with the intent to deceive. Science was born from a yearning to discover how the world around us really works, discarding ancient traditions that commanded "it is so because I tell you so", in favor of demonstrating "this is how it seems to work, see for yourself". Science is not dogmatic but demonstrative and it employs a method that is an extension of common sense.

As an example, most of us are satisfied that germs from the environment may contaminate and eventually rot food and other stuff that are left out in the open, but until not long ago most people thought that things rot spontaneously without external interventions. It took Pasteur and others to show that substances sterilized by heat and kept in a sterile environment remain sterile unless contaminated from outside germs, thus dismissing any thought of spontaneous generation and paving the way to the many food preservation technologies of modern times.

Pasteur did so by conducting tests that distinguished the fortuitous from the essential factors that cause contamination and rot, using instruments and methods of tested reliability and precision. Any test, of course, admits the probability of error and science advances on efforts to reduce error to the point where measurements become sufficiently reliable for the purpose at hand. If the purpose is to inform real life decisions, the level of precision may vary. For instance, a toxic medicine that has two to one chances of curing patients who would otherwise die might be acceptable, whereas a commercial passenger aircraft must secure a probability in the order of less than one failure in 100 million miles in order to be acceptable. In general, scientific findings must have low probability of error for issues affecting the general public, especially in the formulation of public policy.

Ultimately, then, a finding qualifies as scientific if it warrants to measure what it purports to measure rather than some unknown interference, and if the measure is sufficiently accurate. Thus, testability and testing remain the core prerequisites of science: the former is necessary to qualify hypotheses as scientific, the latter to provide assurance of credibility and thus to make possible the advancement of knowledge and its applications, including policy. It follows by definition that science has no interest in hypotheses that cannot be tested, an axiom that should raise a flag when untestable hypotheses are offered as "scientific" especially in what are known as "soft sciences", such as economics, sociology, political science, and others, including the epidemiology of diseases that arise from multiple causes and are said to be multifactorial.

In general, those "sciences" lack a scientific structure because proper tests are so bewildering complex as to be practically impossible, thus making most of their hypotheses untestable. If it were not so, economists would be the richest of men, sociology would have solved mankind's renewing social riddles, and political science would have created perfect government. At this point one may reasonably ask why these activities are called scientific? The most charitable answer is that their practitioners have learned to set up complex mathematical and statistical games, whimsically connected to reality. In truth, though, they are more like the blind men of Indostan meeting the elephant. They can touch it all right, and even measure what they touch with some accuracy, but they cannot say for sure what they are measuring, and their conclusions remain guesswork.

As we shall see, this is precisely the problem with the epidemiologic studies utilized by the EPA in its risk assessment of ETS and lung cancer—a problem that is compounded by the absence of an adequate scientific culture at the agency. This telling deficiency was revealed and highlighted by the blue-ribbon panel previously mentioned and convened by the EPA itself to evaluate the conditions of science at the agency (USEPA, 1992e). The panel released its report in March 1992, with a critique of scathing implications that anticipated the vexing lack of credibility of the EPA's ETS report, finding among other things that:

> [the] EPA does not have a coherent science agenda and
> operational plan to guide scientific efforts throughout
> the Agency.

[the] EPA science is perceived by many people, both *inside and outside the Agency, to be adjusted to fit policy* (Emphasis added).

[the] EPA should be a source of unbiased scientific information. However, [the] EPA has not always ensured that contrasting, reputable scientific views are well explored and well documented from the beginning to the end of the regulatory process.

[the] EPA does not give sufficient attention to validating the models, scientific assumptions and databases it uses.

With such wariness in mind we shall consider the essential EPA claims that ETS is similar to the smoke that smokers inhale (mainstream smoke or MS) and therefore similarly toxic, and that epidemiologic studies confirm ETS as a cause of lung cancer in non-smokers, despite much smaller exposures. Still, the Agency has been unwilling to compare active smokers with non-smokers exposed to ETS on the basis of exposure ratios, because massive exposure differences would reduce non-smoker risk to virtually zero. So it is that throughout the report the EPA equivocates about the similarity of ETS and MS to Judge Osteen's understandable annoyance—invoking or rejecting the similarity as it bolsters arguments that ETS is risky.

As for epidemiology, the agency relied primarily on studies that compare exposure to ETS in groups of people with lung cancer and those without. Such studies raise many problems because exposure to ETS cannot be reliably measured and because many other exposures are causally linked to lung cancer: a multifactorial disease. Biases also arise, for instance from the misclassification of smokers as non-smokers or from the preferential publication of studies that show risk elevation. Without some reliable measure of exposure, and without ascertaining the confounding roles of other causes of lung cancer and of several biases, it may not be possible to reach conclusions about the role of ETS, if any.

These problems do not plague the epidemiology of infectious diseases that occur only after exposure to specific bacteria, viruses, and parasites. Indeed, It would be grossly unfair to lump all epidemiology together in view of the spectacular successes with infectious diseases—successes that have been possible precisely because absolutely undeniable causes could be identified and controlled. This is not the case for the study of most cancers and other conditions that are linked to a multitude of risk factors, none of which could be positively labeled as a cause.

The assessment of the possible role of confounding factors is practically impossible in the case of ETS and lung cancer studies, the upshot being that these studies fall much short of credible science. The problem is common to the study of most multifactorial diseases, to the point that a prominent anti-smoking epidemiologist, Prof. Doll, recognized that such

> [e]pidemiological observations...have serious disadvantages ... [T]hey can seldom be made according to the strict requirements of experimental science and therefore may be open to a variety of interpretations. A particular factor may be associated with some disease merely because of its association with some other factor that causes the disease, or the association may be an artifact due to some systematic bias in the information collection.

Doll continued saying that

> [i]t is commonly, but mistakenly, supposed that multiple regression, logistic regression, or various forms of standardization can routinely be used to answer the question: Is the correlation of exposure (E) with disease (D) due merely to a common correlation of both with some confounding factor (or factors) (C)? ... Moreover, it is obvious that multiple regression cannot correct for important variables that have not been recorded at all.

Doll concluded that

> [t]hese disadvantages limit the value of observations in humans, but ... until we know exactly how cancer is caused and how some factors are able to modify the effects of others, the need to observe imaginatively what actually happens to various different categories of people will remain. (Doll and Peto, 1981, p. 1218)

It should be noted that the key word of the closing phrase is "imaginatively", which tells of the inevitable subjectivity in interpreting reports of multifactorial epidemiology—reports that can only raise conjectures subject to multiple and often contrasting interpretations.

Doll's statements apply to all studies reviewed by the EPA—studies that included a multitude of confounding influences and biases impervious to adequate control, and that cannot be replicated under the same or comparable conditions. Jointly, these deficiencies make it impossible to draw inferences of causality.

Overcoming these problems requires some peculiar reasoning, well characterized by another leading epidemiologist who writes:

> Despite philosophic injunctions concerning inductive inference, criteria have commonly been used to make such inferences. The justification offered has been that the exigencies of public health problems demand action and that despite imperfect knowledge causal inferences must be made. (Rothman, 1986, p. 17)

Clearly, it is a circular argument when the exigencies of public health are invoked to justify those inferences that sustain the exigencies in the first place. For epidemiologists this may be an argument of good intentions (and definitely self-serving) but it is not a scientific one. Yet, it is the very argument advanced by a majority of epidemiologists to justify the astonishing assertion that imaginative perceptions alone are worthy of becoming forcible public policy (Gori, 1998 a,b).

At the same time, it is inevitable that multifactorial epidemiology will continue to raise questions of how to make the best of it. Those questions are of paramount importance for, even though the verification powers of the scientific method may not be available, epidemiologic studies will be performed in societies that are highly sensitive to issues of health and disease, and also highly confrontational and activist on policy matters. In this context, epidemiologic studies will not generate objective scientific conclusions but will continue to produce warnings about potential risks—warnings that in some instances could become legitimate motivators of prudent policies according to the force of their credibility. What criteria should be used to grade this credibility?

Although multifactorial epidemiology could not aspire to be a science, its warnings could be more tenable in proportion to its efforts to approximate a truly scientific test: that is if it made a demonstrable effort to account for as many risk factors as are known, to provide a convincing quantitative measure of exposures, to adopt experimental designs that credibly control for biases, statistical procedures directed at uncovering uncertainties rather than at creating a deceptive impression of precision, and a range of interpretations that covered all possible directions that a final analysis of the evidence might suggest (Gori, 1998a,b).

These should be the core discriminants of the quality of epidemiologic reports that are to inform public health policy decisions. Instead, since as early as 1964 epidemiologists and public health practitioners have opted for a set of muddled, maneuverable, and far less credible guidelines. These are the judgmental criteria initially advanced in the first Surgeon General's report on smoking and later formalized by Hill, and are the now familiar considerations of strength, consistency, specificity, temporality, response gradient, plausibility, coherence, analogy, and experimental evidence. (USSG, 1964; Hill, 1965). Judgmental inferences have been made in situations that met most of these qualifiers, but in reality none of these criteria addresses the core issues of scientific evaluation: namely the influence of biases and confounders as obstacles to causal inference (Schaffner, 1991). In fact, no one has yet proposed a method for an integral evaluation of the combined effects of biases and confounders in multifactorial studies, leading some epidemiologists to warn that risk elevations less than a range from 2 to 5, depending on study complexity, could not be used to infer even hypotheses of causality (Breslow and Day, 1980; Rothman, 1982; Wynder, 1987,1990).

Many if not most multifactorial studies, of which those of ETS and lung cancer are a prime example, do not come close to meeting the fashionable but precarious Hill causality criteria listed above. This has prompted epidemiologists and regulators to invent still more elastic ways to enable unjustifiable inferences of causality, such as the "weight of evidence" approach that the EPA professes to have adopted in making its case against ETS (NAS, 1993; USEPA, 1992c). In theory, this approach entails a lose integration of all pros and cons of a situation, but not the EPA's selective choice of data supportive of its preconceived objectives that provoked Judge Osteen's resentment.

A cornerstone of the EPA's weight of evidence approach has been the use of the meta-analysis procedure in consolidating various epidemiologic reports into a single risk estimate. In reality the use of this procedure is not permissible because meta-analysis is only properly applied to groups of studies that are highly homogeneous, according to guidelines endorsed by the National Cancer Institute and other groups (Blair et al., 1995, Shapiro, 1997,1998). In fact, the editors of the Journal of the National Cancer Institute warned that "[b]iased studies entered into a meta-analysis produce biased results" (Weed and Kramer, 1997).

Unfortunately, the weight of evidence approach does not have clearly articulated rules but only generic admonitions that, ironically, were later spelled out by the EPA in its 1996 proposed guidelines for risk assessment, where it states that in weight of evidence judgments the

> [e]xistence of temporal relationships, consistent results in independent studies, strong associations, reliable exposure data, presence of dose-related responses, freedom from biases and confounding factors, and high level of statistical significance are among the factors leading to increased confidence in a conclusion of causality. (USEPA, 1996)

Belatedly entered in the EPA's books, these requirements could not have been met by the studies of ETS and lung cancer that were the basis for the EPA's 1992 risk claims—which explains in the EPA's words why the Agency's preconceived conclusions could only be arrived at through a weight of evidence approach woefully open to all sort of mischievous assumptions and selectivity, as the following analysis will show.

Chapter Three

The EPA Report on Environmental Tobacco Smoke: Absence of Scientific and Epidemiologic Foundations

Less than 1 in 10 of the ETS and lung cancer studies are of the type known as "cohort studies", where large numbers of people are classified in groups that are or not exposed to ETS. In estimating risk, the frequency of lung cancer in the exposed is divided by the corresponding frequency in the non-exposed: if the two are the same the result is 1 and there is no difference in risk; if the frequency is higher in the exposed the result is greater than 1, suggesting that exposure may increase the risk; if the frequency is greater in the non-exposed the result is less than 1, suggesting that ETS exposure may decrease the risk, namely that it may be protective.

Cohort studies suffer from the many difficulties and uncertainties that we shall soon consider, but by far the majority of ETS and lung cancer studies are of an even more questionable kind known as "case/control studies". These studies compare ETS exposure histories—derived from dubious individual recollections of intensity and duration of exposure over a lifetime—in groups of people with lung cancer (the cases) versus exposure histories in groups of people without lung cancer (the controls). Here, therefore, risk estimates do not reflect differences in disease frequency but rather vague differences of exposure, and risk values are calculated by dividing indices of exposure in lung cancer patients by corresponding indices in the controls: if the two are the same the result is 1 and no risk difference can be inferred; if exposure is greater in cancer patients the result is greater than 1 and suggests inferences of increased risk; if exposure is greater in the controls the result is less than 1 and inferences of reduced risk or protection are possible.

Case/control studies suffer from major credibility problems. In the first place, they can only infer surrogate risks based on uncertain exposure proxies and not on differences of actual disease frequencies. They also compare selected groups of cancer patients with control groups of people without the disease, based on the incredible assumption that the groups are the same except for the degree of exposure to ETS. Further, their results—even if interpretable—cannot have general meaning because the studies are invariably and inevitably small and therefore self-localized, unlike cohort studies that might have larger statistical bases. Still, both cohort and case/control studies present kindred and insurmountable problems of execution and interpretation.

To begin, measuring ETS exposure is often difficult beyond any pretense of objectivity, especially when it relies on the subjective answers of individuals who are asked to recall events going back four or five decades in their lives, or when the information about earlier exposures of deceased subjects comes from the recollections of next of kin. The uncertainties of memory pose unresolvable challenges to a reliable determination of duration and intensity of exposure. Misclassification of smokers as non-smokers is another well recognized obstacle in determining exposure, as the EPA's own report noted (USEPA, 1992c, at 5.5.2).

Persons that have been diagnosed with lung cancer or other diseases have a natural tendency to find or imagine causes, to exaggerate recollections of exposures, and to blame others if there is an opportunity—a clear problem for ETS studies, given that just about every study subject has been intensely exposed for many years to anti-smoking messages that claimed increased lung cancer risk for ETS exposures. By contrast, people free of lung cancer who may serve as the control group in a study will have less incentive to exaggerate, thus producing a differential bias and the artificial appearance of a lung cancer risk (Lee, 1993; Redhead and Rowberg, 1995; Lee and Forey, 1995, 1996; Ogden).

The precise diagnosis of lung cancer presents noticeable difficulties, but even more intractable problems in epidemiologic surveys derive from their very structure. The comparison of ETS exposed and unexposed groups would yield reliable results if the only difference among them were passive smoke exposure, but this ideal situation is nearly impossible because natural groups of individuals differ for much more than ETS exposure alone. Lung cancer, for instance, has been linked to over two dozen risk factors besides cigarette smoking, which terribly complicates any analysis (Thornton et al., 1994; Gori and Mantel, 1991). It is not a boxing match where one individual wins or loses, but rather a ball game where presence at the stadium does not necessarily imply a contribution to victory or loss.

Contrary to media and popular misconceptions, it follows that claims of ETS being a cause of lung cancer are based on surveys of non-smokers that are said to be scientific but are not. Epidemiologists recognize among themselves the lack of science in what they are doing. As a prime example, we have previously quoted Prof. Doll—prominent among anti-smoking epidemiologists—who acknowledges that epidemiology cannot be science and is open to all sort of interpretations (Doll and Peto, 1981. p. 1218.). As we recall, Doll ended up stating that epidemiology must be interpreted "imaginatively" thus emphasizing the want of scientific objectivity in the epidemiology of multifactorial diseases, lung cancer included. Doll's admission gets lost in a professional publication that few read, and epidemiologists studiously avoid letting this little secret appear in public messages that are deceptively described as scientific.

People in a survey may be asked whether they are smokers or not and their answers are assumed to be correct, usually without checking for sure. Epidemiologists may rely on vague distant memories of the extent of exposure to ETS, without checking whether people were also touched by other conditions that seem linked causally with lung cancer: such as a family history of disease, hazardous occupations, poor diets, weight problems, unhealthy homes, lack of exercise and the like. All considered, it is inescapable to conclude that epidemiologists, like the blind men and the elephant, collect and measure some information but cannot tell for sure what they have measured—a situation that is absolutely incompatible with objective science.

What's more, epidemiologic measures usually are extremely inaccurate. To be sure, every measure lacks some precision and even super-accurate atomic clocks register some error, but most measures are sufficiently precise and therefore reliable. For all their complexities, airplanes are built to be reliable for many million miles, and even lowly bicycles function correctly most of the time, and washing machines, telephones, and so forth. But who would accept fastfoods that 1 time out of 20 cause intestinal infections? Or toothbrushes that fall apart after 19 uses? Or cars that 1 time out of 20 turn left when drivers actually steer right? Yet, this is what passes for certainty in epidemiology, where the universal standard of precision admits a 1 in 20 rate of error and more, if the EPA has its way.

The extent of measurement uncertainties that plague epidemiologic reports of passive smoking and lung cancer will be immediately evident in the tables that follow, listing studies available to the EPA in 1992. As a first example of the agency's selectivity, also noted in Judge Osteen's decision, three sets of data were available in 1992: one dealing with non-smoking wives exposed to the ETS of their smoking husbands (spousal studies), one dealing with ETS exposures in workplaces (workplace studies), and one dealing with ETS exposures in childhood (childhood studies). The last two sets did not show an overall elevation of risk and were summarily dismissed by the EPA, even though the EPA's report acknowledges the "widespread presence of ETS both in home and workplace" (USEPA, 1992c, p.1-6). In briefs submitted to the

Court, the agency asserted that childhood and workplace studies had been ignored because ETS exposure could not be measured well enough, and also on account of unspecified confounders. The Court however noted that these were specious justifications because the EPA did not provide criteria for evaluating exposure or confounders, and especially because the same considerations would also apply to exclude the spousal studies that the EPA eventually selected (Osteen, 1998, p. 70). The 31 spousal studies available in 1992 from around the world were patently heterogeneous and difficult to compare, and the EPA itself saw inconsistencies in that only an "overall proportion (9/30) of individual studies [was] found to show an association between lung cancer and spousal ETS exposure at all levels combined" (USEPA, 1992c, p. 1-7). In the end, the EPA looked at international studies but ultimately selected 11 US spousal studies available in early 1992.

Epidemiologic studies utilized by the EPA for the ETS risk assessment

The EPA's list of US spousal studies is found in Table 1 below, giving the names of the lead authors, the year of publication, and the number of persons with lung cancer included in each study. The first values in the last column of Table 1 give the average estimates of relative risks. Any such an average is iffy because the actual value could be higher or lower depending on the uncertainties of measurement. How different the actual value could be is estimated by the last two values in the last column, one lower and one higher than the prior listed average, so that the actual value could be at any point between the low and the high values. For those interested in technical lingo, the range in the last column is the 90 percent confidence interval, meaning there is a 90 percent confidence that a measured value rests in that interval (Breslow and Day, 1980; Mantel and Haenszel, 1959). Hence, two compounded uncertainties become apparent: first, that the actual measure could be anywhere in the confidence interval and, second, that the interval itself could be in error with a 1 in 10 probability. Here, Judge Osteen noted that the agency itself would use 95 percent confidence intervals as the required standard in all its transactions, but adopted an irregular 90 percent interval specifically for the ETS assessment, as a gambit to produce the misleading impression of a nonexistent precision.

   A last word about reading Table 1, keeping in mind again that a reported value of 1 implies no risk, a value greater than 1 implies increased risk, and a value below 1 implies ETS exposure may actually protect against lung cancer. Thus, if the low value in a given confidence

Table 1: Passive smoking and lung cancer in EPA-selected studies of US females who never smoked and were married to smokers.

Author	Year published	Cancer cases	Relative risk & 90% confidence interval	
Brownson	1987	19	1.52	0.49-4.79
Buffler	1984	41	0.81	0.39-1.66
Butler	1988	8	2.02	0.48-8.56
Correa	1983	22	2.07	0.94-4.52
Fontham	1991	420	1.29	1.03-1.62
Garfinkel 1	1981	153	1.17	0.85-1.61
Garfinkel 2	1985	134	1.31	0.93-1.85
Humble	1987	20	2.20	0.90-5.50
Janerich	1990	191	0.86	0.57-1.29
Kabat 1	1984	24	0.79	0.30-2.04
Wu	1985	29	1.41	0.63-3.15

(Data from USEPA, 1992c, Table 5-5)

interval is less than 1 and the high value is more than 1, the result is moot because the actual value could be anywhere in the interval. It could mean either protection or risk elevation and there is no telling one way or another. In those cases the result is said to be nonsignificant, and the last column to the right in Table 1 shows that this is the situation for 10 of the 11 studies listed. On the other hand, if both ends of an interval are above 1 the result implies risk, but Table 1 shows that such is barely the case for one study alone. In fact, none of the studies might have been significant if the agency had used the standard 95 percent confidence interval instead of its irregular 90 percent selection.

The EPA dismissed the need to check and adjust for confounders

The absence of statistical significance is only one of the uncertainties plaguing these studies, but there are more. In assessing the possible role of ETS it is necessary to find out whether other *known* risk factors for lung cancer might be present to confound the situation, and thus impute to passive smoking a role it doesn't have. Table 2 lists the relative values of some of the common risk factors associated with lung cancer as reported in the literature. As before, values greater than 1 imply greater risk, while values less than 1 imply protection.

Table 2: Reported independent risk or protection factors for lung cancer.

Factor	Reference	Reported risk/ protection	95% confidence intervals
Family history of lung cancer	Samet (1986)	5.3	2.2-12.8
	Ooi (1986)	2.4	-
	Horwitz (1988)	2.8	1.0-7.7
	Wu (1988)	3.9	2.0-7.6
	Brownson (1997)	2.7	1.2-6.1
Personal history of tuberculosis	Hinds (1982)	10.0	1.1-90.1
	Gao (1987)	6.4	-
	Wu (1988)	1.7	1.1-2.4
	Sakurai (1989)	8.2	1.3-54.4
β–carotene/vitamin A deficiency	Ziegler (1986)	2.2	-
β–carotene/ vitamin A intake	Wu (1985)	0.3	p=0.06 trend
	Byers (1987)	0.2	-
	Pastorino (1987)	0.4	0.2-0.9
	Candelora (1992)	0.4	0.2-0.8
Alcohol intake	Pollack (1984)	2.19	1.3-5.0
Dietary cholesterol/fat	Goodman (1988)	2.2	1.3-3.8
Dietary fat intake	Wynder (1987)	4-6	-
	Alavanja (1993)	6.14	2.63-14.40
	De Stefani (1997)	2.85	1.73-4.69
Pork meat intake	Mettlin (1989)	2.4	1.4-4.2
Vegetable diet	Le Marchand (1989)	0.6	0.4-0.88
	Jain (1990)	0.3	p=0.009 trend
	Candelora (1992)	0.2	0.1-0.5
	Alavanja (1993)	0.61	0.37-0.99
	Axelsson (1996)	0.37	0.23-0.61
	Sankaranarayanan (1994)	0.32	0.13-0.78
Fruit intake	Koo (1988)	0.4	0.2-0.9
	Candelora (1992)	0.6	0.3-1.1
Milk intake	Mettlin (1989)	2.1	1.4-3.2
	Rylander (1996)	1.73	1.0-3.01
	Axelsson (1996)	1.73	1.0-3.01
Hormone therapy in women	Adami (1989)	1.3	-

Table 2 continued

Factor	Reference	Reported risk/ protection	95% confidence intervals
Cooking methods	Gao (1987)	1.4-2.6	1.1-5.0
	Mumford (1987)	5.6	3.4-9.1
	Geng (1988)	1.9	1.1-3.3
	Sobue (1990)	23	-
	Ko (1997)	8.3	3.1-22.7
Radon	Edlin (1984)	4.3	1.7-10.6
	Lees (1987)	2.4	0.8-7.1
Occupation	Kvale (1986)	2.6	-
Motor exhaust exposure	Hayes (1989)	1.5	1.2-1.9
	Jacobsson (1997)	2.0	1.5-2.6
	Gustavsson (1990)	2.4	1.3-4.5
Socioeconomic class	Brown (1975)	2.6-3.8	-
Ventilatory function	Lange (1990)	24	-
Cardiac anomalies	Tenkanen (1987)	2.4	-
Physical inactivity	Albanes (1989)	1.6	1.2-3.5
	Severson (1989)	1.4	1.0-2.1
Psychosocial traits	Kulessa (1989)	23	-
	Knekt (1996)	3.32	1.53-7.20
Urban/rural risk ratio	Shy (1984)	1.22.8	-
Arsenic ingestion	Tsuda (1995)	15.69	7.38-31.02
Vitamin E intake	Yong (1997)	0.36	016-0.83
High education	van Loon (1997)	0.53	0.34-0.82
Vitamin A,C and E intake	Yong (1997)	0.32	0.14-0.74
Vegetables/fruit intake	Agudo (1997)	0.45	0.22-0.91
Asbestos exposure	Oksa (1997)	10.0	6.9-14.0
	Zhu & Wang (1993)	5.32	-
	Dement (1994)	2.3	1.88-2.79
	Raffin (1993)	3.31	-
Physical activity	Thune (1997)	0.39	0.18-0.85
	Lee & Paffenbarger (1994)	0.39	0.18-0.85
Beer drinking	Potter (1992)	2.0	1.02-3.8

For instance, a personal history of tuberculosis is a major risk factor for lung cancer, but a diet rich in vegetables is associated with strong protection. At the same time Table 2 can be interpreted in the obverse, where for instance the absence of a history of tuberculosis means less risk, while a diet poor in vegetables means increased risk. Table 2 lists the actual published reports and is for readers interested in the record at large. For those interested in risks at a glance, Figure 1 summarizes and ranks the major risks of Table 2. Both table and figure attest to the much greater force and universal statistical significance of these risk factors, compared to the weak and non-significant ETS associations claimed in Table 1. Such a difference in strength means that even a slight differential influence of extraneous risks could easily corrupt ETS risk estimates and render them uninterpretable.

Thus, in considering what may cause a disease it is important to distinguish between true causes and factors that are simply associated with a disease. For example, most of us are satisfied that a virus is the cause of influenza, but until not long ago people believed that influenza was caused by bad air, the cold of winter, the evil eye, and so forth. Scientists, however, inquired further and were able to show that influenza is not possible without the virus, no matter what other circumstances. Cancer also was seen until recently as a dreaded disease of mysterious nature and origin, and scientists have come close to clarifying what cancer might be—the nature of cancer—but have been not nearly as successful in uncovering its causes. The reason is that, unlike influenza and other infectious diseases, cancer is many different diseases, triggered not by some evil magic bullet but by clusters of many possible causes whose individual role is unclear—clusters so variable that we can talk of risk factors but not of specific causes.

From a stance that is both scientific and common sense, to inquire about the actual causal significance of any one of these factors requires knowing what the individual significance of all others might be: a task that in practice cannot be carried out without confusion. That is why these factors are called confounders in epidemiologic studies of smoking and lung cancer. Here again Prof. Doll, the influential epidemiologist on smoking and health issues, had to admit that

> ... [active] smoking seems to act synergistically with other aetiologic agents such as consumption of alcohol; various aspects of the diet; levels of blood pressure, blood lipids, or other cardiovascular risk factors; or exposure to asbestos, radon, or possibly some infective factors. The quantitative effect of smoking will, therefore, vary with variation in the prevalence of these other factors. (Doll et al., 1994)

Figure 1: Rank order of reported lung cancer risk factors

1. Hormone therapy	_1.30
2. Motor exhaust	_1.50
3. Physical inactivity	_1.60
4. Milk intake	__2.10
5. Alcohol	__ 2.19
6. β-carotene deficiency	___2.20
7. Cholesterol	___2.20
8. Cardiac anomaly	____2.40
9. Low fruit	____2.40
10. Pork meat intake	_____2.50
11. Occupation	_____2.60
12. Urban/rural	_____2.80
13. Psychosocial traits	_____2.90
14. Low vegetable intake	_____3.00
15. Beer drinking	_____3.20
16. Socioeconomic class	_____3.40
17. Ventilatory function	_____3.50
18. Radon	_____4.00
19. Family history	_____5.30
20. Cooking methods	_____5.50
21. Dietary fat	_____6.0
22. Asbestosis	_____9.0
23. Tuberculosis	_____10.0
24. Smoking	_____10.0

Adapted from Gori and Mantel, 1991

What Doll did not say is that the prevalence of those other factors is not known, nor could it be known without first understanding the quantitative significance of smoking.

Clearly, then, if the quantitative assessment of the effects of active smoking requires an accurate account of confounders, such an account is even more necessary when investigating the possible effects of ETS, for these would have to be very much weaker and thus more susceptible to confounding. Therefore, the strength of the lung cancer risks listed in Table 2 and Figure 1 makes it imperative that their potential influence be carefully investigated, since even a slight imbalance of their prevalence between exposed and nonexposed subjects could invalidate a risk assessment for passive smoking. Such imbalances are in fact certain, and several studies have shown that smokers in general display lifestyles that include peculiar risk factors other than smoking: for instance they may exercise less, consume more alcohol, have less healthy diets, more hazardous occupations, lower incomes and education, and so forth. Moreover, studies have ascertained that the less healthy habits and risks of smokers are shared with non-smoking members of a household and non-smoking wives in particular (Gori and Mantel, 1991; Le Marchand, 1991; Margetts and Jackson, 1993; Cress et al., 1994; Lee and Fry, 1994; Matanoski et al., 1995; Emmons, 1995). With this in mind, it is no surprise that apparent risks for ETS exposure have been noted only in non-smoking wives of smokers.

Studies of smoking and non-smoking households have shown that corrections for differences of beta carotene intake alone can reduce to near statistical insignificance the risk attributed to ETS (Sidney et al., 1989; Le Marchand et al., 1989, 1991; Thornton et al., 1994). Therefore, the slight apparent attributions of risk to ETS could easily disappear after cumulative correction for other risk factors clustering in smoking households (Lee, 1998). In reality, however, the studies listed in Table 1 and utilized by the EPA for its risk assessment of ETS either checked the possible influence of confounders in the most perfunctory way, or not at all. Table 3, taken directly from the EPA report, indicates this clearly.

Despite the very sparse and unsatisfactory attention to confounders in the US spousal studies, the EPA report came to the surprising conclusion that no confounding factor "... explains the association between lung cancer and ETS exposure ... " (USEPA, 1992c, at 5.4.8). This arbitrary and wholly inadequate conclusion is typical of the *ipse dixit*, one-sided gambits the agency displays over and over in dismissing or trivializing crucial difficulties that are in its way. Yet another example is how the agency disposed of the obstacles posed by differential biases.

The EPA trivialized the likely influence of differential biases

One undisputed but difficult to measure bias is known as the publication bias, whereby studies reporting risk have a better chance of being published in epidemiologic journals (Easterbrook, 1991; Blair, 1995; Saracci, 1995; Lee, 1992; Givens, 1997; Armitage, 1997). As early as 1975, Greenwald found that some 6 percent of researchers were inclined to submit negative results, against 60 percent that would do so with positive ones (Greenwald, 1975). The potential effects of this bias were essentially ignored by the EPA.

Table 3: Control of possible confounders in EPA-selected studies of passive smoking and lung cancer risk in US females who never smoked and were married to smokers.

Author	Year	Adjusted risk factors
Brownson	1987	Occupation, socioeconomic status
Buffler	1984	None
Butler	1988	None
Correa	1983	Smoking
Fontham	1991	Urban/rural living, socioeconomic status
Garfinkel 1	1981	Occupation, socioeconomic status
Garfinkel 2	1985	Socioeconomic status
Humble	1987	None
Janerich	1990	Urban/rural living
Kabat 1	1984	None
Wu	1985	Urban/rural living

(Data from USEPA, 1992c, Table 5-6)

Arguably a greater problem is presented by the misclassification bias previously mentioned, which tells that if even a small proportion of study subjects with lung cancer had been smokers but falsely declared to be and to have been non-smokers, then exposure to ETS could erroneously show as a lung cancer risk. The EPA report freely recognizes that "[t]here is ample evidence that some percentage of smokers ... misrepresent themselves as never-smokers ... " (USEPA, 1992c, at 5.2.2), and Table 4 lists the extent of this misclassification, as measured in a sample of studies not considered by the EPA but mostly available to the agency at the time the ETS report was being compiled.

None of the US spousal studies utilized by the EPA contains information that could permit one even to guess the extent of misclassification. This omission in itself prevents the drawing of any conclusion as to the role of ETS in lung cancer especially in view of the substantial reports of misclassification from other studies listed in Table 4. The obstacle was again overcome by the EPA under cover of an elaborate procedure that pretended to calculate a misclassification index for each of the studies involved on the basis of arbitrary assumptions—a procedure that predictably trivialized the probable impact of misclassification by ending up with a compound misclassifi-

Table 4: Misclassification in self-reported non-smokers

Author	%	Author	%
Ohlin, 1976	12-32	Hatziandreu, 1989	28
Vogt, 1977	>15	Klesges, 1992	4.2
Sillett, 1978	22-40	Wagenknecht, 1992	4.2
Cohen, 1980	7-19	Perez-Stable, 1992	6.3
Jarvis, 1987	19	Brownson, 1993	6-16
Stookey, 1987	25-55	Delfino, 1993	>5
Coultas, 1988	7-10	Murray, 1993	6

cation index of 1.09 (USEPA, 1992c, at 5.2.2). Studies published after the EPA's report confirm higher misclassification rates than those used by the agency, and show that a misclassification rate of only 3 percent could reverse the EPA's estimate to one of *reduced* risk (Lee and Forey, 1995; Ogden et al., 1997; Phillips et al., 1996 to 1998; Lee, 1998).

The EPA "cherry-picked" studies, arbitrarily ranked their importance, and relaxed statistical standards to reach its preconceived objectives

The EPA also presumed to give different weight to different studies according to arbitrary tiers of utility, affirming that " ... [s]tudy utility does not mean study quality. Utility is evaluated with respect to the research objectives of this report" (USEPA, 1992c, p. 5-14). Elsewhere, the objectives of the EPA report are clarified as being " ... based on the *a priori* hypothesis that a positive association exists between exposure to ETS and lung cancer" (USEPA, 1992c, p. 5-2). In other words, the objective of the report was to prove the agency right when it affirmed that ETS causes lung cancer, an objective that the EPA also secured by assigning better weights to the studies favorable to its intent.

Moreover, a determination to reach its objective at all costs led the agency to ignore unilaterally the possibility of reduced risk (protection?) implied by the average values of three of the studies of Table 1 and by the prevailing absence of statistical significance. As we saw, the agency fixed this problem by adopting 90 percent confidence intervals and statistical procedures that admitted only the consideration of elevated risk: a gimmick that doubled the margin of error from 1:20 to 1:10, in sharp contrast to the accepted conventions of epidemiology and medicine, and the standard procedures of the EPA itself.

The EPA concluded its risk assessment with an improper meta-analysis, and reached a false estimate of casualties with preposterous precision

Even allowing for statistical gambits, three of the studies utilized by the EPA in 1992 imply a protective effect of ETS but are not statistically significant, eight imply an elevation of risk but are also not statistically significant, and one was barely a marginal exception. From a scientific point of view the only tenable conclusion is that no conclusion is possible, but the EPA was determined to have its way and resorted to a final piece of meta-analysis trickery, to condense in a single risk value the results of the available spousal studies. As we mentioned, the meta-analysis procedure has legitimate uses in the consolidation of data from studies that have been planned and conducted according to common study design, selection of participants, data collection and processing methods. Such might be the case for a group of clinical trials, but hardly for ETS studies. The procedure is not legitimate when applied to diverse studies that lack homogeneity, where it would be equivalent to the familiar comparison of apples and oranges (Shapiro, 1998; Blair et al., 1994; Lee, 1998). Further, most ETS studies report more than one risk calculation depending on different segmentations of the data, and therefore the meta-analysis selection of a particular risk value representative of a given study is in itself an arbitrary decision, as the EPA itself openly admits (USEPA, 1992c, at 5.2.1).

Among other differences, the US spousal studies differ in geographic location, time of execution, provenance and selection of cases and controls, matching of controls, questionnaire format and content, direct and proxy sources of information, diagnostic procedures, methods of adjustment and data handling. An even greater diversity of the studies derives from differences in exposure recall rates and precision, different and unknown rates of misclassification, and the impact of different confounders of different strength in each study. Overall there are enough differences to conclude that a meta-analysis summation of ETS studies would be an impermissible instrument of either technical illiteracy or deceit, open to the manipulation of so many slanted assumptions.

In a final cavalier gesture, the EPA introduced an upward "correction" of ETS risk based on its *a priori* assertion that ETS must be a lung cancer risk. It argued that study subjects who reported no exposure to ETS would be nevertheless exposed to some ubiquitous background ETS level that would expose them to the lung cancer risk that the EPA had dogmatically asserted. On this basis the agency introduced an upward "correction" in producing an estimate of the U.S. annual lung cancer cases presumably attributed to ETS. It did so on the basis of a convoluted sequence of untestable assumptions, admitting in fine print that the results were " ... based on calculations in which unknown parameters are replaced by numerical estimates that are subject to uncertainty" (USEPA, 1992c, p. 6-31). In effect the uncertainty surrounding those estimates must be extreme, because the entire argument for upward correction is voided by the absence of overall risk elevation in workplace and childhood studies, whose subjects are unquestionably exposed to ETS at far more than background levels.

In the end, it should be obvious that the accumulation of uncertainties and arbitrary assumptions can only qualify the EPA report on ETS as an exercise in selective wishful thinking. To top it all, the agency adopted further assumptions and announced with preposterous precision that ETS is responsible for 3060 lung cancer cases a year in the US alone a figure that has been amplified by advocacy and regulatory interests to justify an unprecedented social engineering crusade of worldwide intolerance.

The agency proceeded on its course even though internal reviewers from the EPA's Cincinnati laboratories were highly critical of the agency's approach and conclusions (USEPA, 1992d). The EPA's Science Advisory Board itself—the highest advisory committee to the agency—advised the agency against producing numerical estimates (Stolwijk, 1993), and Dr. Erich Bretthauer, Associate Administrator for Research and Development at the EPA in 1992, had to admit in official correspondence that the excess risk of lung cancer could be virtually zero (Bretthauer, 1992). Also, two assessments by the Congressional Research Service of the Library of Congress reached equally critical conclusions (Gravelle and Zimmermann, 1994; Redhead and Rowberg, 1995).

Evidence that discounts the possibility that ETS could be a risk for lung cancer

Does ETS compare to the smoke that smokers inhale?

Implicit in the EPA's position is that ETS is similar to the smoke that smokers inhale and therefore carries a similar risk, albeit reduced because of reduced exposure. This parallel was first proposed in the Surgeon General's report on ETS, the NAS and IARC reports of 1986, and other assessments that have considered the concept of "cigarette equivalents" to link the risk of ETS to that of MS (the mainstream smoke of active smoking) by scaling down in proportion to the amount of smoke inhaled. However, the EPA has been decidedly equivocal on this issue. At times it stated that the similarity of MS and ETS "is sufficient in its own right to establish the weight of evidence for ETS as a Group

A (known human) carcinogen ... " (USEPA, 1992 c, p. 2-9), but elsewhere it has denied this possibility because the

> differences in physicochemical properties of main-
> stream smoke and sidestream smoke (the principal
> component of ETS), in lung dosimetry between active
> and passive smoking, and in exposure patterns (related
> to the concentration and duration of exposure) are not
> fully understood, but the current state of knowledge
> casts doubts on the validity of these assumptions.
> (USEPA, 1992c, p. 6-30)

This important issue obviously demands closer scrutiny, beginning with considerations about the nature of passive smoke.

ETS comes from the dilution of side-stream smoke (SS) produced by smoldering cigarettes, and from small residues of MS exhaled by active smokers. Generated and existing under much different conditions, ETS, SS, and MS share some similarities but also present marked differences in chemical and physical composition and behavior. All are composed of a gas phase and microscopic droplets known as respirable suspended particles (RSP), the latter eventually forming what is known as tar. These particles in turn may contain at various times different amounts of water and other volatile components that may evaporate and exchange with the gas phase.

The smoke inhaled directly by smokers (MS) maintains higher gas phase concentrations. It also favors larger respirable particles that condense and retain more water and other volatile components, as they are confined with little dilution to the high humidity environment of mouth, throat, and lung. By contrast, ordinary ETS is some 100,000 times more diluted in drier ambient air. Evaporation is faster from ETS particles, which within fractions of a second from their generation shrink to sizes 50 to 100 times smaller in mass and volume than their MS counterparts by losing water and volatile components to ambient air. As ETS ages, it undergoes oxidative and photochemical transformations, polymerizations, further loss of water and volatiles, reactions with other environmental components, and other changes (Table 5) (NAS, 1986; USSG, 1986; USEPA, 1992c, pp. 3-1, 3-53; Guerin et al., 1987; Baker and Proctor, 1990).

Some 40 agents of mainstream smoke are suspected of being carcinogenic in experimental animals (Hoffmann and Hecht, 1989), and the EPA report implies that those agents are present in ETS as well (USEPA, 1992c, p. 2-1), even though this affirmation remains a conjecture unsupported by actual detection and measurement. These agents may have shown carcinogenicity in animal organs other than the lungs, at doses

Table 5: Some differences of mainstream smoke (MS), side-stream smoke (SS), and environmental tobacco smoke (ETS).

Characteristics	MS	SS	ETS
Measured components	>4000	<100	< 20
Temperature	900 C	600 C	Ambient
Oxygen	20%	2%	Ambient
Pyrolysis products	High	Low	Low
pH	≈6.5	≈7.0	Ambient?
Photochemical transformations	Low	Medium	High
Polymerizations /oxidations	Low	Medium	High
Dilution	20	10^2	10^{5-6}
Humidity	High	Ambient	Ambient
Age	3-5 sec	3-5 sec	Hours
Particle diameter	≈1 μm		≈0.1 μm
Particle volume	≈0.5 μm^3		≈0.005 μm^3
Volatiles and water in particles	High	Medium	Very Low
Lung retention efficiency	90%		10%

(Data from Guerin et al., 1987; USEPA. 1992c)

much larger than smokers can experience, and with clear and repeated evidence of doses that produce no observable effect, namely a no-effect threshold. At the same time, and faithful to its one-sided approach, the EPA report does not mention other components of mainstream and side-stream smoke that are known to suppress carcinogenesis, and are also present at dose ratios similar to those found effective in suppressing experimental cancer (Rodgman, 1992; Teel and Castonguay, 1992; Van Duuren, 1980).

Of the several thousand components identified in mainstream smoke, only about 100 have been detected in side-stream smoke under real-life conditions, due to extreme dilutions. Because of even greater dilution, fewer than 20 ETS components have been identified directly in real-life settings, although a few more might have been detected under controlled laboratory conditions (USEPA, 1992c, p. 3-10). The EPA displays a baffling ambiguity about this issue, because at times it recognizes the dearth of analytical data on ETS, and at others it affirms that ETS "is a complex mixture of over 4,000 chemicals found in both vapor and particle phases" (USEPA, 1992c. p. 3-15). In reality, whatever they might be, most components of real-life ETS are far below the sensitivity of current analytical capabilities and cannot be detected (Guerin et al., 1987; Baker and Proctor, 1990). The EPA itself states that

> [d]etailed chemical characterization of ETS emissions under conditions more typical of actual smoking conditions (e.g. using smokers rather than smoking machines) are limited. As a result, the impact of ETS on factors such as the rapid dilution of SS emissions, absorption and remission of contaminants, and exhaled MS are not well understood. (EPA, 1992c, p. 3-10)

Indeed, the compilers of reports from the National Academy of Sciences (NAS, 1986), the US Surgeon General (USSG, 1986) and the EPA report itself (USEPA, 1992c) have arbitrarily inferred the presence of ETS components by proxy, based on the composition of the side-stream smoke from which ETS primarily derives, and without considering that many chemicals change nature as they dilute and interact with the environment. In a rare moment of candor, the difficulties in determining what ETS is all about led the EPA report to note that "[t]he rapid dilution of both [side-stream smoke] and [mainstream smoke] into the environment and changing phase distributions of ETS components over time raise some questions about the carcinogenic potential of ETS under actual environmental exposure conditions" (USEPA, 1992c, p. 4-29).

Nominally, then, ETS and mainstream smoke may share some components, but their chemical and physical differences are substantial. Moreover, the presence of most ETS components can only be postulated because they are beyond material detection, to the point of raising serious doubts about the plausibility of ETS being a lung cancer risk, as the EPA itself notes. These doubts are further reinforced by some opportunities to gauge ETS exposures and doses relative to their counterparts in active smoking.

Comparing ETS and MS exposures

The limitations of epidemiologic studies on ETS result in major uncertainties that are compounded by the problems of recalling the cumulation of intensity, frequency, and duration of exposures over individual lifetimes. As mentioned before, the actual information is obtained either directly from the subjects of study, or through next of kin proxies when the subjects are deceased. Both sources present problems besides the common difficulty of recalling exposures that might have occurred 30 or 40 years earlier, because direct respondents especially people with lung cancer may be understandably prone to emphasize and lay blame on ETS, while next of kin answers may be more candid but also more vague about lifetime exposures of deceased relatives.

Even a simple dual classification of ETS exposed and non-exposed subjects presents recognized uncertainties, such as those deriving from the misclassification of some smokers as non-smokers, as previously seen (USEPA, 1992c; Lee, 1992, 1993). On grounds that are less problematic, a range of probable momentary exposures to ETS can be inferred from physical and chemical derivations. These inferences also are insufficient to determine or validate individual cumulative exposures, but raise compelling doubts about the reliability and meaning of epidemiologic estimates.

On the basis of extrapolations from side-stream and mainstream smoke data, the National Academy of Sciences calculated that for nicotine alone the difference in peak inhalation concentrations between smokers and ETS exposed non-smokers varies between 57,000 and 7,000,000 fold (NAS, 1986). Dose estimates based on body fluid concentrations of nicotine or cotinine yield lower differences, but depend on environmental and pharmacokinetic assumptions of unlikely validity because nicotine adsorbs and desorbs from curtains, carpets, clothing, and the like, even in the absence of ETS. Nicotine may also be ingested from certain vegetables, and is likely to be eliminated from the body at progressively slower rates as its blood concentration declines (USEPA, 1992c, at 3.3.1.1; Domino, 1993, Benowitz et al. 1991; Collier at al., 1992: Van Loy et al., 1997).

Estimates of exposure to other gaseous ETS components are just as problematic because they could also derive from numerous sources external to ETS. For instance, plasma concentrations of volatile organics in non-smokers appear to be as much as 2/3 of the corresponding levels in active smokers—an indication of significant sources other than tobacco combustion (Angerer et al., 1992; Brugnone et al., 1992; Perbellini et al., 1988).

In any event, assuming that ETS emissions of chemical species are similar to those of mainstream smoke, they would end up producing ambient air concentrations that are orders of magnitude below levels permitted as safe in workplaces by the American Council of Governmental and Industrial Hygienists and the Occupational Safety and Health Administration. By utilizing surrogate side-stream smoke values, possible ETS exposures have been compared with current federal standards of permissible occupational exposure to several smoke components. Considering an unventilated room of 100 m³ (3,533 cubic feet), Table 6 shows the number of cigarettes that would have to be burned before reaching official threshold limit values (TLV). The burning of 1,170 cigarettes would be necessary to reach TLV for methylchloride, 13,300 for benzene, 222,000 for benzo(a)pyrene, 1,000,000 for toluene (Gori and Mantel, 1991). The absurdity of these numbers becomes apparent when realizing that TLVs are levels of exposure permitted for lifetime employment, based on a normal 8 hour daily work shift.

It has been argued that comparing ETS with official TLV values may not be feasible because TLV values are intended for single agent exposures and not for mixtures. This distinction, however, is invalid for two reasons. First, workers are never exposed to single agents but to mixtures in any environment, whether workplace or not. Second, valid parallels can indeed be made for TLV values issued for mixtures such as coke oven emissions that may share components with side-stream smoke and possibly with ETS. To complete this picture, it should be kept in mind that the safety of federal workplace standards is ensured by considerations of prudence that have reduced permissible TLV levels much below what could be considered technically safe exposures. Thus, either federal workplace safety standards are grossly wrong—which they are not—or the EPA claims of ETS hazard are inconceivable.

There are other ways to assess the immaterial nature of ETS exposures. As we have noted, both mainstream smoke and ETS contain microscopic particles suspended in gases (respirable suspended particles or RSPs). Those particles eventually end up as constituents of tar and are thought to represent the fraction of smoke that contains the most undesirable components. On this point, a review by the International Agency for Research on Cancer stated that "[e]xperiments on the carcinogenicity of the gaseous phase of cigarette smoke in hamsters and rats resulted in negative or inadequate findings ... " signifying that risk assessments should place a greater weight on RSPs than on other components (IARC, 1986, p. 195). This is especially valid since measurements of RSPs have been more fruitful than the measurement of single chemical species, if nothing else because RSP are the most material component of ETS that can be collected and approximately weighed. Methods have been devised to separate particles that may derive from ETS and from other sources, and measurements had persuaded the EPA itself that prevailing concentrations of ETP-RSP are below 50 $\mu g/m^3$ (micrograms or millionths of gram per cubic meter) in situations comparable to households with smokers—namely the environments of the epidemiologic studies that the EPA has considered in assessing ETS (USEPA, 1992c, p. 3-34). Table 7 reports ETS-RSP concentration data available to the EPA in 1992, although more recent and more refined measurements, which utilized personally worn collectors of particulates under real life conditions, suggest that the average concentration of ETS particulates is probably less than 20 $\mu g/m^3$, including conditions of spousal exposures (Gori and Mantel, 1991; Samet, 1992; Steenland, 1992; Haevner et al., 1996; Jenkins et al., 1996; Sterling et al., 1996; Phillips et al., 1994 to 1998).

Table 6: Number of cigarettes needed to reach Threshold Limit Values (TLV) for selected components of side-stream smoke (SS) in a sealed and unventilated 100 m^3 enclosure (from Gori and Mantel, 1991).

SS component	SS output* mg/cigarette	TLV** mg/m^3	Cigarettes required
Methylchloride	0.88	0.30	1,170
Hydroquinone	0.16	2.00	1,250
Cadmium	0.0007	0.01	1,430
Acetaldehyde	1.26	180.00	1,430
Acetic acid	1.50	25.00	1,660
Nitrogen oxides	2.80	50.00	1,780
Formic acid	0.525	9.40	1,790
Pyridine	0.39	16.00	4,100
Phenol	0.25	19.00	7,600
Methylamine	0.1	13.00	13,000
Benzene	0.24	32.00	13,300
Catechol	0.14	23.00	16,500
Nickel	0.0025	1.00	40,000
Dimetylamine	0.036	18.00	50,000
Hydrazine	0.00009	0.13	145,000
Acetone	1.00	1780.00	178,000
Benzo(a)pyrene	0.00009	0.20 ***	222,000
2-Toluidine	0.003	9.00	300,000
Polonium 210	0.4 pCi	3 pCi/l****	750,000
Toluene	0.000035	375.00	1,000,000

* Data from EPA 1990a, Table C-2, page C-19, 20.
** Data from ACGIH 1990.
*** Based on the TLV for coal tar pitch volatiles.
**** EPA 1990b.

Because ETS particles are some 100 times smaller that MS particles, the EPA itself recognizes that only about 10 percent of inhaled ETS particles may be retained by non-smokers, compared to nearly 90 percent retention for mainstream smoke particles in active smokers (USEPA, 1992c, p. 3-3). Furthermore, lung clearance is faster and more efficient in non-smokers than in smokers, and the amounts deposited on single lung cells are far smaller because smaller ETS particles reach greater depths in the lungs, where they are dispersed on a much larger

Table 7: Some reports available to the EPA in 1992 of respirable suspended particles (RSP) concentrations from ETS and other sources in various environmental settings with and without smoker presence. (from Gori and Mantel, 1991).

| Reference | Site | RSP concentration $\mu g/m^3$ | |
		No smoking	Smoking
Coultas et al. 1990a	Homes	NA	17
Sheldon et al. 1989	Homes	22**	65**
Spengler et al. 1981	Homes	NA	20
Spengler et al. 1985	Offices	39*	72**
Proctor et al. 1989b	Offices	8*	23*
Oldaker et al. 1990	Offices	NA	27*
Miesner et al. 1989	Offices	15**	36**
Sterling et al. 1983	Offices	15**	29**
Coultas et al. 1990b	Workplaces	NA	64**
Oldaker et al. 1990	Restaurants	NA	36*
Crouse 1988	Restaurants	NA	34*
Proctor 1990	Public transit	14*	36*

* Based on UVRSP portion of total RSP
** Based on total RSP
NA—Data not available

number of cells that eventually extend to an average surface approaching some 1000 square feet (Mercer and Crapo, 1993; Gori and Mantel, 1991).

Overall, these considerations lead to the conclusion that the prevalent dose of ETS particles is minuscule. Although difficult to define, Table 8 indicates that prevalent ETS doses could be well over 100,000 times smaller than prevalent doses in active smokers, a conclusion that the EPA studiously avoided even though it could have been reached from data available to the agency in 1992 and listed in its report (USEPA, 1992c). For the average ETS-exposed individual, this estimate translates into a dose equivalent to actively smoking slightly more or less than 1 cigarette evenly dispersed over the period of 1 year, a conclusion confirmed by more recent studies that employed more precise techniques and different methodologies (Haevner et al., 1996; Jenkins at al., 1996; Sterling et al., 1966; Phillips et al., 1994 to 1998).

Considering the average smoker of 30 cigarettes per day (USEPA, 1992c, p. 1-11), the question then is whether ETS could pose plausible risks to non-smokers who experience immaterial exposures compared to active smokers.

Table 8: Relative dose estimate of respirable suspended particles (RSP) in typical active smokers and ETS exposed non-smokers.

Active smoker	30 cigarettes per day [*]
	15 mg RSP inhaled per cigarette
	90% lung retention efficiency [*]
	Daily dose about 400 mg
ETS exposed non-smoker	0.05 mg RSP/cubic meter of air [*]
	1.5 hours per day exposure [**]
	0.7 cubic meters per hour inhaled [*]
	10% lung retention efficiency [*]
	Daily dose about 0.00525 mg

Crude dose ratio 0.00525 : 400 or about 1 : 75,000

Lung surface permeability some 3 times greater in smokers [***]
Lung clearance some 3 times more efficient in smokers [***]
ETS dose distributed over greater surface deeper in lungs [***]
Plausible dose ratio at target tissue   < 1 : 500,000

(*) USEPA, 1992c, p.1-11.
(**) USOSHA, 1994; Emmons et al., 1992.
(***) Gori and Mantel, 1991.

Could minute ETS exposures pose a risk of lung cancer?

The estimate of ETS health risks by derivation from the apparent risks associated with active smoking was both supported and opposed in the EPA report (USEPA, 1992c). The report dedicates a chapter to the proposition that: "... due to the similarity in chemical composition between [mainstream smoke] and ETS and the known human exposure to ETS ... , ETS would also be classified as a ... human carcinogen" (USEPA, 1992c, p. 4-10). Elsewhere we have seen that the report lists the many differences of mainstream smoke and ETS, suggesting that risk extrapolation from active smoking may not be feasible (USEPA, 1992c, p. 2-7). A direct comparison based on the "cigarette equivalent" approach also has been questioned by other ETS opponents (Steenland, 1992). In reality, the only plausible inferences would come from the measurable differences of particulate exposures reported in Table 8. Accordingly, the health risks of ETS if any would have to be so much

Table 9: Estimating lung cancer deaths (LCD) in active and passive smokers using the EPA's attributed risks and demographic parameters.

Data from USEPA, 1992c

Average ETS dose compared to smokers *	$A = 10^{-4}$ to 10^{-5}
Active US smokers	$B = 5 \times 10^7$
LCDs in smokers	$C = 1.12 \times 10^5/\text{year}$
LCD rate in smokers	$D = C/B = 2.24$ by 10^{-3}
ETS-exposed US non-smokers	$E = 6.907 \times 10^7$
Estimated ETSLCDs	$F = 3.06 \times 10^3/\text{year}$
LCD rate in ETS-exposed non-smokers	$G = F/E = 4.43 \times 10^{-5}$

EPA assumptions	Linear kinetics, no threshold
therefore	If the EPA's ETS risk rate is applied to smokers
Smoker LCDs/year	$(G \times B)/A = 22.15 \times 10^6$ to 221.51×10^6
Conversely	If smokers' risk is applied to non-smokers
Non-smoker LCDs/year	$D \times A \times E = 1.54$ to 15.47 (?)

* Figures from Table 8.

smaller as to be unmeasurable, when compared to the risk associated with mainstream smoke.

The absurd implications of the EPA's claims can be seen in Table 9, which shows that if the EPA conclusions regarding ETS risk to non-smokers were to be applied to smokers in proportion to their greater exposure, then all US smokers would succumb to lung cancer in less than one year. Conversely, using the lung cancer rate of US smokers, the ETS dose differential could support a possible handful of lung cancers in non-smokers. The latter is in itself a conjecture that would disappear if we consider that the lung cancer risk attributed to smokers is an excessive estimate and would be substantially reduced if adjusted for the many other lung cancer risk factors that Doll acknowledges, as noted before (Doll and Peto, 1994). Accordingly, a downward adjustment of smokers' risk could reduce to virtually zero the hypothetical ETS-attributed extrapolations of Table 9.

Low levels of active smoking are compatible with no risk for lung cancer and negate the plausibility of ETS risk

An additional argument against the EPA's claims derives from the observation that smokers who smoke very few cigarettes daily may show no appreciable risk compared to non-smokers. Thus, it is inconceivable that ETS exposures could be a risk, being thousands of times below the still trivial exposure of smoking a few cigarettes daily. To appreciate this argument one should keep in mind that although the mainstream smoke that active smokers inhale contains substances that are carcinogenic in animal experiments, the epidemiology and pathogenesis of lung cancer has suggested to prominent investigators—not friendly to tobacco—that smoking may act as a promoter or helper rather than as a direct carcinogen (Doll, 1978; Doll and Peto, 1978; Klawansky and Fox, 1984; Altshuler, 1989; Albert, 1989). Promoters are universally regarded as being effective only after certain dose thresholds are exceeded, and active smoking appears to be no exception.

For mainstream active smoking the epidemiologic risks associated with certain diseases become nonsignificant at low exposures. Persons who inhale a daily equivalent of 3-4 cigarettes may not attain lung cancer risks significantly different from those of non-smokers, as Table 10 shows, where the figures are obtained by regression of epidemiologic dose-response data and are given as the upper limits of 95 percent confidence intervals whose lower limits are null risk values, as is common in regulatory practice (Gori, 1976; Gori and Mantel, 1991; Gaylor et al., 1977). It is also of interest that the studies in Table 10 pertain to smokers of pre-1960 cigarettes with average tar yields over 25 milligrams per cigarette, nearly twice as much as the average for current cigarettes. Conceivably, the difference could make for even higher thresholds than those listed in table 10, when related to current cigarettes.

It could be argued that this reasoning may be invalid if smokers of 3-4 cigarettes daily are atypical and do not inhale. This objection falls, however, when realizing that the threshold values of Table 10 come not from observations in such smokers, but are statistical extrapolations determined by the continuum of smoking intensity observations, from the highest to the lowest. Thus, values in Table 10 are valid composite derivations defined by the risks of smokers at all levels of daily cigarette consumption (Gori and Mantel, 1991).

No-effect observations at comparatively high doses are also routinely reported in experimental animal exposures to whole smoke or its fractions, and an evaluation of the EPA's ETS report by the Congressional Research Service of the Library of Congress also recognized the reality of no-effect thresholds, as follows:

> The existence of an exposure threshold for disease onset below which many passive smokers fall is not implausible. Most organisms have the capacity to cleanse themselves of some level of contaminants. It is

Table 10: Maximum levels of daily cigarette consumption at which lung cancer risk in male smokers may not be significantly increased from the risk of non-smokers (from Gori and Mantel, 1991).

Reference	Max. cigarettes/day
British Doctors*	6.3
Swedish Men**	3.9
ACS 9 States***	5.4
ACS 25 States**	0.9
US Veterans***	0.6
Canadian Veterans***	1.6
Japanese Men**	3.1
California Men***	7.0

* Doll and Peto, 1978
** USSG, 1979. page 513 table 2.
*** USSG, 1982. page 38 table 6.

> for this reason that public policy usually does not insist that every unit of air or water pollution be removed from the environment ... In fact, strongly nonlinear relationships in which health effects rise with the square of exposure, and more, have been found with respect to active smoking (see Surgeon General's Report, 1989, p. 44). Were these relationships projected backwards to construct the lower (unknown) portion of the health effect/physical damage function, the observed relationship might lead researchers *a priori* to expect no empirical relationship. Thus, the issue raised by this potential break in the causative chain is whether researchers should expect to find a significant relationship between passive smoking and health effects. (Gravelle and Zimmermann, 1994, p. 45)

No-observable-adverse-effect-levels (NOAEL) for active smoking have a disposing relevance in the evaluation of claimed ETS risks. They are apparent in routine extrapolations from epidemiologic dose/response data as reported in Table 10, and are also directly observable in epidemiologic studies. For instance, a compendium of 34 year follow-up data recently published for the Framingham study—the longest and most closely monitored epidemiologic study of its kind in the United States, which followed every aspect of the lives of several thousand people in that community—reports that adjusted lung cancer rates were not elevated for smokers of 1-10 cigarettes/day below age 65 (Freund et al., 1993). Similarly, the British Doctors study in England is widely regarded as the best continuing study outside the United States, and perhaps the best in the world. In this study, lung cancer mortality rates were the same in non-smokers and in smokers of 1-14 cigarettes/day. Mortality from all diseases was actually slightly lower in smokers of 1-14 cigarettes/day than in non-smokers (Doll et al., 1980).

To these reports one should add the evidence that moderate pipe and cigar smoking are not associated with increased risks of lung cancer and other diseases (USSG, 1964). In this light, prevalent ETS exposures roughly equivalent to the active smoking of one cigarette per year are a thousand or more times below exposures that result in no significant health risks for active smokers.

It could be argued that comparing exposures to respirable suspended particles of MS and ETS is problematic because the nature and composition of the two tars are likely different. Still, the argument would have no force if the biologic activity of ETS-RSP were the same or lower than that of MS-RSP—which is plausible—while the argument could have meaning only if the specific biologic activity of ETS-RSP were a thousand times greater than for MS-RSP, clearly an unsupportable conjecture. Altogether then, consideration of the vast exposure and dose differentials indicate that ETS could not pose ponderable health risks, even assuming that ETS may be chemically and biologically equivalent to mainstream smoke.

Epidemiologic studies published after 1992 do not sustain the claim that ETS poses a lung cancer risk in non-smokers

ETS studies published after the 1992 EPA report on ETS further reinforce the conclusion that the EPA's attribution of 3060 lung cancers a year to ETS is based on unwarranted assumptions, selective use of data, procedural manipulations, and the contrived illusion of numerical precision.

The arbitrariness of the EPA's claims is highlighted by the agency's dismissal of the two latest studies available in mid 1992, which were funded by the National Cancer Institute and reported data at some odds with the Agency's conclusions (Stockwell et al., 1992; Brownson et al., 1992). It is interesting to dwell on these two latest studies and the single study that the EPA considered to be of the highest significance (Fontham et al., 1991). The Brownson abstract states that the study results justify smoking restrictions in work places, but the study itself shows a reduction of risk for workplace exposures, a finding shared with the Stockwell study but opposed by the Fontham study. Brownson and Fontham find that childhood exposures to ETS may *reduce* lung cancer risk, but Stockwell disagrees. The studies are discordant on diagnostic histopathology results. The Stockwell study reports elevated risk if cancer patients were interviewed directly, but a *reduction* of risk if next of kin were interviewed. Indeed, the studies register a long list of internal contradictions that parallel those of all available studies, again signifying that the selection of a single risk value representative of each study is, without doubt, an arbitrary exercise.

Several more studies of ETS exposures and lung cancer have been published since the 1992 EPA report and have yielded consistently equivocal results. Successive US spousal studies have yielded progressively smaller meta-analysis risks, while studies of lung cancer and ETS exposure in childhood or in the workplace have continued to sustain the possibility of a *reduction* of risk. Published ETS and lung cancer studies available in mid 1998 are given in Tables 11, 12, and 13. Here too the listed average risk values are iffy because actual values could be higher or lower than the average, depending on the uncertainties of measurement. As previously noted, the actual value could be at any point between the low and the high values of the 95 percent confidence intervals. We are again observing two compounded uncertainties: the first that the actual measure could be anywhere in the confidence interval and, the second, that the interval itself could be in error with a 1 in 20 probability.

As previously noted, risk values below 1 associate ETS exposure results with decreased risk and vice versa. Therefore, if the low value in a given confidence interval is less than 1 and the high value is more than 1, the result is moot because the actual value could be anywhere in the interval and there is no telling whether the risk is increased or decreased. In those cases the result is said to be non-significant, and the last column to the right in the tables shows that this is by far the most common circumstance.

The many reports available in 1998 clearly show how the epidemiologic message remains hopelessly garbled. If one were to use the EPA's procedures biased toward obtaining elevated risk, the meta-analysis of US spousal studies might still suggest a very slight elevation of risk around 1.07, although fully one third of the individual studies suggest a reduction of risk (Lee, 1998). The precariousness of guessing this risk elevation is again apparent when realizing that the studies are heterogeneous to the point of precluding a legitimate meta-analysis, and that none of the studies has controlled for a credible variety of confounders, nor has provided credible misclassification measures. In regard to the latter alone, one should keep in mind that a guess of slight risk elevation for current US spousal studies is only possible if one relies on

Table 11: Epidemiological studies of lung cancer among non-smokers married to smokers.

Author	Year	Location	Sex	Number of lung cancers	Relative risk & 95% confidence intervals	
Garfinkel 1	1981	USA	F	153	1.18	0.90-1.54
Chan	1982	Hong Kong	F	84	0.75	0.43-1.30
Correa	1983	USA	F	22	2.07	0.81-5.25
			M	8	1.97	0.38-10.32
Trichopoulos	1983	Greece	F	77	2.08	1.20-3.59
Buffler	1984	USA	F	41	0.80	0.34-1.90
			M	11	0.51	0.14-1.79
Hirayama	1984	Japan	F	200	1.45	1.02-2.08
			M	64	2.25	1.19-4.22
Kabat 1	1984	USA	F	24	0.79	0.25-2.45
			M	12	1.00	0.20-5.07
Garfinkel 2	1985	USA	F	134	1.23	0.81-1.87
Lam W	1985	Hong Kong	F	60	2.01	1.09-3.72
Wu	1985	USA	F	29	1.20	0.50-3.30
Akiba	1986	Japan	F	94	1.50	0.90-2.80
			M	19	1.80	0.40-7.00
Lee	1986	UK	F	32	1.00	0.37-2.71
			M	15	1.30	0.38-4.39
Brownson 1	1987	USA	F	19	1.68	0.39-6.90
Gao	1987	China	F	246	1.19	0.82-1.73
Humble	1987	USA	F	20	2.20	0.80-6.60
			M	8	4.82	0.63-36.56
Koo	1987	Hong Kong	F	86	1.64	0.87-3.09
Lam T	1987	Hong Kong	F	199	1.65	1.16-2.35
Pershagen	1987	Sweden	F	70	1.20	0.70-2.10
Butler	1988	USA	F	8	2.02	0.48-8.56
Geng	1988	China	F	54	2.16	1.08-4.29
Inoue	1988	Japan	F	22	2.25	0.80-8.80
Shimizu	1988	Japan	F	90	1.08	0.64-1.82
Choi	1989	Korea	F	75	1.63	0.92-2.87
			M	13	2.73	0.49-15.21
Hole	1989	Scotland	F	6	1.89	0.22-16.12
			M	3	3.52	0.32-38.65
Svensson	1989	Sweden	F	34	1.26	0.57-2.81
Janerich	1990	USA	F	144	0.75	0.47-1.20
			M	44	0.75	0.31-1.78
Kalandidi	1990	Greece	F	90	2.11	1.09-4.08

Table 11 continued

Author	Year	Location	Sex	Number of lung cancers	Relative risk & 95% confidence intervals	
Sobue	1990	Japan	F	144	1.13	0.78-1.63
Wu-Williams	1990	China	F	417	0.70	0.60-0.90
Liu Z	1991	China	F	54	0.77	0.30-1.96
Brownson 2	1992	USA	F	431	1.00	0.80-1.20
Stockwell	1992	USA	F	62	1.60	0.80-3.00
Liu Q	1993	China	F	38	1.66	0.73-3.78
Du	1993	China	F	75	1.09	0.64-1.85
Fontham	1994	USA	F	651	1.29	1.04-1.60
Layard	1994	USA	F	39	0.58	0.30-1.13
			M	21	1.47	0.55-3.94
Zaridze	1994	Russia	F	162	1.66	1.12-2.46
Kabat 2	1995	USA	F	67	1.08	0.60-1.94
			M	39	1.60	0.67-3.82
Schwartz	1996	USA	F	185	1.10	0.72-1.68
			M	72	1.10	0.60-2.03
Sun	1996	China	F	230	1.16	0.80-1.69
Wang SY	1996	China	F	82	2.53	1.26-5.10
Wang TJ	1996	China	F	135	1.11	0.67-1.84
Cardenas	1997	USA	F	150	1.20	(0.80-1.60)
			M	97	1.10	0.60-1.80
Jöckel-BIPS	1997	Germany	F	53	1.58	0.74-3.38
			M	18	1.58	0.52-4.81
Jöckel-GSF	1997	Germany	F	242	0.93	0.66-1.31
			M	62	0.93	0.52-1.67
Ko	1997	Taiwan	F	105	1.30	0.70-2.50
Nyberg	1997	Sweden	F	89	1.20	0.74-1.94
			M	35	1.20	0.57-2.55
Boffetta	1998	Europe	M&F	649	1.14	0.88-1.47
			F	508	1.15	0.86-1.55
		Sweden	M&F	70	2.29	0.65-8.07
		Germany 1	M&F	76	0.88	0.40-1.95
		Germany 2	M&F	142	1.22	0.66-2.2
		Germany 3	M&F	31	2.01	0.71-5.67
		England	M&F	26	1.38	0.43-4.28
		France	M&F	77	0.72	0.36-1.25
		Portugal 1	M&F	49	2.04	0.71-5.80
		Portugal 2	M&F	33	2.03	9.76-5.38
		Spain	M&F	71	1.10	0.48-2.68
		Italy 1	M&F	40	0.73	0.28-1.65
		Italy 2	M&F	19	1.12	0.35-3.56
		Italy 3	M&F	16	1.36	0.30-6.45
Jöckel	1998	Germany	M&F	71	1.12	0.54-2.32

Table 12: Epidemiological studies of lung cancer among non-smokers exposed to ETS in the workplace.

Author	Year	Location	Sex	Relative risk & 95% confidence intervals	
Kabat 1	1984	USA	F	0.68	0.32-1.47
			M	3.27	1.011-0.62
Garfinkel 2	1985	USA	F	0.93	0.55-1.55
Wu	1985	USA	F	1.30	0.50-3.30
Lee	1986	UK	F	0.63	0.17-2.33
			M	1.61	0.39-6.60
Koo	1987	Hong Kong	F	1.19	0.48-2.95
Shimizu	1988	Japan	F	1.18	0.70-2.01
Janerich	1990	USA	F&M	0.91	0.80-1.04
Kalandidi	1990	Greece	F	1.70	0.69-4.18
Wu-Williams	1990	China	F	1.10	0.90-1.60
Brownson 2	1992	USA	F	0.79	0.61-1.03
Stockwell	1992	USA	F	not statistically significant	
Fontham	1994	USA	F	1.39	1.11-1.74
Zaridze	1994	Russia	F	1.23	0.74-2.06
Kabat 2	1995	USA	F	1.15	0.62-2.13
			M	1.02	0.50-2.09
Schwartz	1996	USA	F&M	1.50	1.00-2.20
Sun	1996	China	F	1.38	0.94-2.04
Wang TJ	1996	China	F	0.89	0.46-1.73
Jöckel-BIPS	1997	Germany	F&M	2.37	1.02-5.48
Jöckel-GSF	1997	Germany	F&M	1.51	0.95-2.40
Ko	1997	Taiwan	F	1.10	0.40-3.00
Nyberg	1997	Sweden	F&M	1.60	0.90-2.90
Boffetta	1998	Europe	M&F	1.17	0.94-1.45
			F	1.19	0.94-1.51

the EPA's 1992 methods and its assumptions of arbitrarily low misclassification rates. However, it is of note that a conservative misclassification rate of only 3 percent—modest in relation to the higher misclassification reports in the literature, as listed in Table 4—would change by itself alone the meta-analysis result of current US spousal studies to an estimate of *reduced* risk (Lee, 1998). It should be amply evident how any conclusion is extremely sensitive to selected assumptions.

Table 13: Epidemiological studies of lung cancer among non-smokers exposed to ETS in childhood.

Author	Year	Location	Sex	Relative risk & 95% confidence intervals	
Correa	1983	USA	F	not statistically significant	
Garfinkel 2	1985	USA	F	0.91	0.74-1.12
Wu	1985	USA	F	0.60	0.20-1.70
Akiba	1986	Japan	F&M	not statistically significant	
Gao	1987	China	F	1.10	0.70-1.70
Koo	1987	Hong Kong	F	0.55	0.17-1.77
Pershagen	1987	Sweden	F	1.00	0.40-2.30
Svensson	1989	Sweden	F	3.30	0.50-18.80
Janerich	1990	USA	F&M	1.30	0.85-2.00
Sobue	1990	Japan	F	1.28	0.7-12.31
Wu-Williams	1990	China	F	0.85	0.65-1.12
Brownson 2	1992	USA	F	0.80	0.60-1.10
Stockwell	1992	USA	F	1.70	1.00-2.90
Fontham	1994	USA	F	0.89	0.72-1.10
Zaridze	1994	Russia	F	0.98	0.66-1.45
Kabat 2	1995	USA	F	1.63	0.91-2.92
			M	0.90	0.43-1.89
Sun	1996	China	F	2.29	1.56-3.37
Wang TJ	1996	China	F	0.91	0.56-1.48
Jöckel-BIPS	1997	Germany	F&M	1.05	0.50-2.22
Jöckel-GSF	1997	Germany	F&M	0.95	0.64-1.40
Ko	1997	Taiwan	F	0.80	0.40-1.60
Boffetta	1998	Europe	M&F	0.78	0.64-0.96
			F	0.77	0.61-0.98

Further, the overall meta-analysis of workplace and childhood exposures continue to suggest reduced risk or protection. The EPA discounted studies suggesting risk reduction, claiming that they are unreliable or represent statistical flukes, as opposed to the studies that suggest risk elevation. Of course this is nonsense, because if the actual risk is null we would expect some studies to show risks somewhat less than 1 and some slightly above 1, and it is no surprise that more studies show above 1 because elevated risk reports have a better chance of being published on account of publication bias (Dickersin, 1997).

In the end—and even after setting aside the fundamental injunctions against causal inferences that derive from the unavoidable structural flaws of cohort and case/control studies—attributions of epidemiologic risk to ETS cannot be rationally sustained unless confounders and biases have been convincingly controlled, and adjustments have been transparently justified. Unfortunately, a satisfactory control of confounders and biases is beyond technical feasibility, and ETS epidemiologic studies in general do not hold sufficient promise as profitable investments of scarce research funds. Simply stated, epidemiologic studies are not sensitive and specific enough to justify ETS investigations. So it is that the EPA's assertion or even a hypothesis that ETS is a cause of lung cancer are not scientifically justified. They are refuted by the extreme overall weakness of risk signals that are either elevated or reduced, and by studies that cannot warrant to have measured what they purport to have measured, on account of uncontrolled biases and confounders.

Conclusion

Vast differences in exposure intensity and duration preclude inferences of ETS risks, unless we are prepared to forgo all we have learned since Paracelsus about the absence of harm or even the possible beneficial effects of low exposures to otherwise toxic agents. Indeed, exposure to any and all substances could be harmful and even lethal at appropriate high doses.

Plausible ETS exposures are many thousands of times less than exposures that appear to have no adverse effect in active smokers, and studies in man or animals do not contradict this observation, which is reinforced by the equivocations of epidemiologic studies. The latter are impotent in controlling for a multitude of confounders, are plagued by irresolvable biases, and are consistent with slightly increased or decreased risk. By science's standards, the weight of direct and indirect evidence does not sustain the EPA's hypothesis that ETS is a cause of lung cancer in non-smokers.

The only tenable summation is that ETS risks are probably null or imponderable and beyond detection, and that a case against ETS as a lung cancer risk cannot be made on defensible scientific grounds. Thus, it is on the basis of indefensible conjectures that the EPA has unleashed a *de facto* regulatory frenzy and a crusade of hateful cultural and social discrimination against smokers in the US and worldwide.

There is no doubt that ETS is for many an irritating annoyance and the source of idiosyncratic syndromes, the predictable outcome of two decades of a ruthless crusade of public disinformation, pushing the deception that ETS is the number one public health enemy. Certainly

ETS should be of concern to personal courtesy and respect for others, but it would be a sad day when elementary conventions of civility are allowed to be usurped by self-serving bureaucracies and zealots in the name of imaginary anxieties they have managed to foment.

Chapter Four

The Decision: An Analysis

Introduction

On the face of it the Osteen decision appears to be simply another piece of the seemingly unending stream of tobacco litigation: Flue-Cured Tobacco Cooperative Stabilization Corporation, et al., Plaintiffs, v. United States Environmental Protection Agency, Defendant. The language is difficult, the arguments complex and technical, and the issue itself appears completely disconnected from the lives and concerns of ordinary citizens. But behind Judge Osteen's carefully measured words, behind even the specific controversy which the judgment addresses are issues of enormous significance to every citizen of a democratic society who relies on his government to tell him the truth. For the Osteen decision at its core is about truth: it is about how the government uses science to determine whether something constitutes a risk to our health; it is about how the scientific processes for finding truth and the administrative processes for disseminating truth can be corrupted; and it is about the public policy consequences of institutionalizing such corrupt science. This analysis begins with a discussion of the concept of corrupt science, then turns to the regulatory process issues addressed by the decision, and finally examines the substantive scientific issues of the decision.

Corrupt science

Inasmuch as we wish to argue that the Osteen decision supports the characterization of the EPA's ETS process and science as corrupt science, it is important to be clear at the outset about what constitutes corrupt science. By corrupt science we mean bogus science, science that knows that its data misrepresent reality and its processes are deviant, but that nonetheless attempts to pass itself off as genuine science. It is science that has an institutionalized motivation and justification for allowing ends extrinsic to science to determine the findings of science, for allowing science to be subject to an agenda not its own, for allowing science to tell lies with clear conscience. It is essentially science that wishes to claim the public policy advantages of genuine science without conforming to the scientific process or doing the work of real science. While the terms "corrupt science" or "junk science" include the word science, it should be emphasized that this is a courtesy that is not deserved. Corrupt science is really not science at all since it does not have the characteristics of science. It is really pseudo or fake science masquerading as the genuine article.

There are at least four characteristics of corrupt science. First, corrupt science is science that moves not from hypothesis and data to conclusion but instead from mandated acceptable conclusion to selected data back to mandated/acceptable conclusion. It is science that starts with a conclusion, indeed, starts with a mandated policy and sees its job as that of finding and presenting only that evidence that is considered supportive of that conclusion. That is to say, it is science that fundamentally distorts the scientific process through using selected data to reach the 'right' conclusion, a conclusion that by the very nature of the data necessarily misrepresents reality.

Second, corrupt science misrepresents the nature of what it seeks to explain. Rather than acknowledging alternative evidence, or problems with its evidence that would cast doubt on its conclusions, and rather than admitting the complexity of the issue under review and the limits of the evidence, corrupt science presents what is at best a carefully chosen partial truth as the whole truth necessary for public policy. In effect, public policy is manipulated into reaching certain conclusions on the basis of data that has been fabricated, falsified, misrepresented, or massaged so as to speak in a fashion that is fundamentally at odds with the way things really are. Corrupt science in this sense is, according to Teich and Frankel,

> the scientific counterparts of what lawyers call "sharp practices": ... incomplete citation of previously published work; bias in peer review of ... manuscripts; or skewed selection of data to hide or disguise observations that do not fit the author's conclusions ... (Teich and Frankel, 1992, p. 4)

Third, corrupt science not only misrepresents reality but also misrepresents its own processes in arriving at its conclusions. Instead of acknowledging the selectivity of its processes and the official desire for demonstrating predetermined conclusions, it invests both its processes and its conclusions with a mantle of indubitability. It hides, as it were, behind what both fellow scientists and the public believe the scientific process to be, and in doing so it builds an aura of respectability around a decidedly disreputable process. The results appear to be reliable because the process appears to be objective, open, and candid—in short scientific. The selective, the arbitrary, the irrational, and the contrived appear to be certifiably absent since the process is "scientific." Substance and process are thus mutually supporting and taken together the scientific findings that result from the pseudo scientific process present a formidable barrier to public policy dissent.

Fourth, whereas legitimate science creates a climate in which debate and dissent is welcome, in which disagreement is dealt with on the basis of the quality of its evidence and argument and in which *ad hominem* argument is considered inappropriate, corrupt science seeks to create formidable institutional barriers to dissent through excluding dissenters from the process of review, characterizing dissent as working against the public interest, and contriving to silence dissent not by challenging its scientific merits but by questioning its character and motivation.

These four characteristics of corrupt science manifest themselves in a variety of ways which include: claiming that a statistical association is a causal relationship; a highly selective use of data; fabrication of data; falsification of data; misrepresentation of data; selective citation and referencing; claiming that a risk exists regardless of exposure level; claiming that a large number of statistically non-significant studies constitute a significant evidentiary trend; claiming that a series of inconclusive or weak studies justify a strong conclusion; relaxing generally accepted statistical conventions without compelling reasons; being unwilling to consider non-conforming data seriously; implying that the status of an authority justifies its evidence independently of the strength of that evidence; suggesting that weak evidence warrants decisive regulatory action; claiming that a finding based on one population is necessarily true of a different population; suggesting that certain risks are exempt from the normal regulatory and public policy process; and conjoining the roles of the public policy advocate and scientist.

The issues

The issues in dispute center on the EPA's 1992 report, *Respiratory Health Effects of Passive Smoking: Lung Cancer and Other Disorders*, in which the EPA, using the authority provided to it under the Radon Gas and Indoor Air Quality Research Act of 1986, examined the health effects of ETS and classified it as a Group A carcinogen (USEPA, 1992c). Classification as a group A carcinogen meant that the scientific evidence supported the conclusion that ETS causes lung cancer in human beings. The plaintiffs argued that both the process used by the EPA to examine the health effects of ETS, and its finding that ETS causes cancer in human beings were flawed. Specifically, the plaintiffs alleged that: the EPA exceeded its statutory authority under the Radon Research Act; the EPA failed to follow the Radon Research Act's procedural requirements; the EPA

violated established administrative law procedures by reaching a conclusion about the health effects of ETS before conducting its scientific
examination of the evidence; and the EPA's classification of ETS as a
Group A carcinogen was not the product of reasoned science and
decision-making.

The process issues

The process questions involved at least three separate issues: the extent
of the EPA's authority under the Radon Research Act; the nature of the
Radon Research Act's procedural requirements and the EPA's conform-
ity to these requirements; and the question of whether the EPA reached
a decision about the health effects of ETS before beginning the scientific
process, and whether such a decision violated administrative law procedures.

EPA authority under the Radon Research Act

The language of the Radon Research Act appears, at least within the
statutory context, to be relatively straightforward. Yet, as Judge Osteen
observed, the parties reading the same plain language of the Act, came
"to opposite conclusions" as to its meaning (Osteen, 1998, p. 8). The Act
authorizes the EPA to establish a research program on radon and indoor
air quality which has three components: research and development
concerning the identification, characterization, and monitoring of the
sources and levels of indoor air pollution; research relating to the effects
of indoor air pollution and radon on human health, and dissemination
of information to assure the public availability of this research (Osteen,
1998, p. 4). The Act does not authorize the EPA to establish any regulatory program based on the research conducted under the Act. In order
to assist it in discharging its responsibilities under the Act, the EPA is
required to create two advisory groups; one of which is to be made up
of representatives of federal agencies which are concerned with indoor
air quality, and the other of which is to be made up of "individuals
representing the States, the scientific community, industry, and public
interest organizations" (Osteen, 1998, p. 5). As the Court notes, the
purpose of the Act was for the EPA to provide Congress and the public
with clear, objective information about indoor air quality and the effects
of indoor air quality on human health (Osteen, 1998, p. 10) The Act was
not intended to provide regulatory authority to the EPA: the EPA's role
was neither that of advocate of certain positions nor of public policy
maker. Rather, the EPA was to create a research program that would
result in clear, neutral information about indoor air quality.

The plaintiffs did not dispute the right of the EPA to establish a research program on the possible effects of ETS on indoor air quality. They did, however, contest its authority to engage in a carcinogen risk assessment and classification on the grounds that these are regulatory actions that go beyond the authority of the Radon Research Act. The Court, however failed to accept this line of argument.

> The court disagrees with Plaintiffs' argument that risk assessment constitutes a regulatory activity and is thus prohibited under the Radon Research Act. Both the NRC's (National Research Council) Redbook and [the] EPA's Risk Assessment Guidelines identify regulatory activity as being comprised of two elements: risk assessment and risk management. Prohibition of certain conduct does not include prohibition of lesser included activities. (Osteen, 1998, p. 15)

Moreover, the Court noted that the Radon Research Act also contains specific directives to the EPA that warrant its carcinogenic classifications.

> First, Congress required the EPA to characterize sources of indoor air pollution ... Since they emit gasses and particulates, burning cigarettes are a source of indoor air pollution. By determining whether these emissions cause cancer in people exposed to burning cigarettes, [the] EPA is characterizing a source of indoor air pollution. Second, Congress required the EPA to determine indoor pollutant effects on health ... In determining whether health is affected by a pollutant, the researcher must identify whether a causal relationship exists between the pollutant and deteriorating health. Put simply, the researcher must determine how, if at all, a pollutant affects health. Once a researcher has identified how a pollutant harms human health, the risk is most often identified. This is especially true regarding carcinogens. The Radon Research Act's general language authorizing [the] EPA to characterize sources of pollutants, research effects on health, and disseminate the findings encompasses classifying pollutants based on their effects. (Osteen, 1998, pp. 12-13)

Thus, the Court found that the Radon Act by providing authority for characterizations of indoor pollutants and their possible health consequences, provides authority for the EPA to engage in risk assessment. As the Court noted, "the Act requires more of the EPA than merely describing effects. Congress intended [the] EPA to disseminate findings, or conclusions, based upon the information researched and gathered. Utilizing descriptions of health effects to make findings is risk assessment" (Osteen, 1998, p. 12). While the EPA is not provided with authority to engage in risk management, it is allowed to conduct risk assessments.

The Radon Research Act's procedural requirements and the EPA

The Radon Research Act requires that the EPA create two advisory groups to assist it in its research and other statutory activities. One of these groups is to be "comprised of individuals representing the States, the scientific community, industry, and public interest organizations ..." (Osteen, 1998, p. 5) The plaintiffs alleged that the EPA failed to comply with this requirement of the law. The EPA replied that it met its procedural obligations by consulting with its own Science Advisory Board.

Before considering the Court's analysis of this issue it is important to be clear precisely what is at stake here. In one sense this is a narrow legal argument about the conditions that satisfy a procedural requirement of the law. But in another sense there is something far more important at stake. The process requirements for risk research and assessment are not incidental or peripheral to the research or the risk classifications that result from such a research process. Indeed, they are integral inasmuch as adherence to accepted scientific processes and standards serves to preserve the integrity of the research findings.

In framing the legislation, the U.S. Congress understood that if science is to preserve its transparent and objective role in the public policy process it must follow a process that was itself transparent and objective. In effect, because of the danger of the scientific process being subverted by a non-scientific agenda, the scientific process needs to occur in an arena in which all voices are heard and no position is excluded *a priori*. The Congress' mechanism for ensuring the legitimacy of the scientific process was to have that process occur within, and be accountable to, a representative body that included all, not just some of those likely to be effected by the research and any consequent regulation. As Judge Osteen noted:

> The most important aspect is the requirement of consultation with knowledgeable representatives of federal and state government, industry and labor. This goes far beyond the usual requirements of public notice and opportunity for comment set forth intake Admin-

istrative Procedure Act, and represents the Congressional answer to the fears expressed by industry and
labor of the prospect of unchecked federal administrative discretion in this field. These rather unique
requirements of the Act are an important part of the
ultimate legislative compromise, and must be given
their due weight. (Osteen, 1998, p. 32)

The representative advisory group serves then as an important
check on the corruption of science in that, by bringing everyone to the
table and then structuring its research program and determining its risk
assessment on the record, the advisory group dramatically reduces the
opportunities for process manipulation, *a priori* policy determination,
data misrepresentation and evidentiary selectivity. The failure to comply with the Radon Act's process requirements is not simply a legal
quibble: failure to comply goes to the heart of the question of whether
the EPA's research and risk assessment on ETS is an instance of corrupt
science.

The EPA did not deny that it failed to create the required advisory
group, and Judge Osteen noted that the "EPA's procedural failure
constitutes a violation of the law" (Osteen, 1998, p. 37) The crucial
question is, why would the Agency act in a way so clearly in violation
of the law? We would suggest that the EPA failed to create a representative advisory group because such a group would have: first,
objected to and made transparent the improper research and risk assessment process to which the EPA was committed; and second, prevented
the ETS carcinogen classification. There are three pieces of evidence that
support this conclusion.

First, the EPA obviously understood how the advisory group would
operate and what was at stake by forming an advisory group. At a
minimum, as Judge Osteen noted, an advisory group would have
ensured that the research and risk assessment processes were on the
record, preventing the gaps in the record that raise what the judge calls
the "ugly possibility" about inappropriate methodology and selective
evidence. By failing to create an advisory group the EPA allowed itself
to work in the dark, to work, both literally and figuratively, off the
record.

But by failing to create an advisory group, the EPA also ensured the
exclusion from its research and risk assessment processes of critics of its
ETS position, which in this case included many others in addition to the
tobacco industry. In effect, there would be no contradictory voices, no
disturbing dissent to the predetermined scientific process. The Tobacco
Institute's attorney, John Rupp, complained to assistant administrator
William Rosenberg about the procedural unfairness of ignoring the

industry's role in the research and risk assessment process, noting that "at no time has there been an opportunity for a scientific discussion of fundamental issues regarding ETS" (Kluger, 1996, p. 693). But, of course, the process corruption was deliberate: the EPA had no interest in having a "scientific discussion of fundamental issues" with anyone who might provide compelling and credible evidence against its pre-determined position.

Second, the EPA, realizing that its manipulation of the research and risk assessment process looked like an attempt to justify a pre-determined position, attempted to mislead the Court about the steps it did take to ensure industry representation. The EPA told the Court that it "formed an advisory group within the [Science Advisory Board] which included representatives of all the statutorily identified constituencies" (Osteen, 1998, p. 21). This group, the Indoor Air Quality/Total Human Exposure Committee (IAQC), according to the EPA, contained three members (out of nine) who represented the tobacco industry. But the Court concluded that this was not in fact true.

> [The] E.P.A. claims that one of the listed members, Dr. Woods, represented industry. However, this is not possible since Dr. Woods left industry for employment with a university almost a year before the first draft of the ETS Risk Assessment was made available for review by IAQC. [The] EPA further asserts that two other individuals represented industry. The ETS Risk Assessment IAQC listing does not contain the names of these individuals. The individuals are not listed in the IAQC ETS reviews, transcripts, ... nor does [the] EPA assert or direct the court's attention to evidence that these individuals provided any participation in the ETS Risk Assessment. (Osteen, 1998, p. 27-28)

The EPA's contention that Dr. Woods represented the tobacco industry, even though he had taken up an academic appointment, is an interesting one in that it appears to represent a belief that one can never really leave the industry, that even whilst no longer in the industry's employ one's views will be industry views. The same peculiar notion underlies the EPA's further claim to the Court that, because certain members of the IAQC were "associated with organizations that had received some industry funding pursuant to contract", they could be considered industry representatives. (Osteen 1998, p. 28) As the Court observed, this "does not convert these individuals into industry representatives" (Osteen, 1998, p. 28). Moreover, even if the IAQC had functioned in the way the EPA claimed, it would have, according to the Court, been a poor proxy for industry representation. [The] EPA sought parties near the "middle" of the spectrum when establishing SAB panels and alleged avoided representation from either end of the spectrum. As a general rule, the tobacco industry occupies that end of the spectrum contesting the carcinogenicity of ETS and [the] EPA['s] motives. A committee aspiring to represent the middle of the ETS debate necessarily suppresses the tobacco's industry's perspective. Further, industry's ability to submit comments to a "neutral" committee, which itself had access to [the] EPA, is not equivalent to industry access to [the] EPA. (Osteen, 1998, p. 32)

But of course the EPA did not wish for the industry to have access for its process corruption was precisely designed to "necessarily suppress" the industry's perspective and participation in the research and assessment activities. Despite the EPA's claims, the record shows the IAQC did not and indeed could not function as the required advisory group since its representation did not include industry and its parties were chosen on the basis on their occupying positions near the middle of the spectrum.

The third and strongest piece of evidence supporting the claim that the EPA failed to create the required advisory group because such a group would have exposed and opposed its fraudulent research and assessment program is the fact that the Agency came to the conclusion that ETS was a human carcinogen prior to beginning its research and risk assessment process. Indeed, this is the clearest piece of evidence for the claim that the EPA's entire work with respect to ETS is an instance of corrupt science inasmuch as it reveals both that the EPA moved from policy/risk assessment (ETS causes cancer in humans) to research rather than vice versa, and that the Agency attempted to conceal this. As Judge Osteen noted:

Rather than reach a conclusion after collecting information, researching, and making findings, [the] EPA categorized ETS as a "known cause of cancer" in 1989 (EPA, Indoor Air Facts No. 5 Environmental Tobacco-Smoke, ANR-445, June,1989) ... [The] EPA's Administrator admitted that [the] EPA "managed to confuse and anger all parties to the smoking ETS debate ... " The Administrator also conceded, "Beginning the development of an Agency risk assessment after the commencement or work on the draft policy guide gave the appearance of ... policy leading science ..." (Osteen, 1998, p. 88)

Having already reached a conclusion about ETS in the absence of the required research program, the EPA could simply not risk using the legally required advisory group. At the very least such a group with tobacco industry membership would leave a public record of vigorous scientific debate about the risks of ETS to human populations, a debate that might well leave both the public and the scientific community skeptical about the EPA's conclusions. At the most, a duly constituted advisory group might actually be so unconvinced by the Agency's conclusions that it would overturn them. As the Court observed, there is a clear "logic" to the EPA's pattern of conduct that was driven by the recognition that there was simply too much at stake to risk the possible interference in a pre-determined policy process of an advisory group.

> [The] EPA publicly committed to a conclusion before research had begun, excluded industry by violating the Act's procedural requirements; adjusted established procedure and scientific norms to validate the Agency's public conclusion, and aggressively utilized the Act's authority to disseminate findings to establish a *de facto* regulatory scheme intended to restrict Plaintiffs products and influence public opinion. (Osteen, 1998, pp. 89-90)

It is simply not credible then that the EPA did not note the significance of its action in failing to create the required advisory group.

The substantive issues

It is possible, of course, that the process corruptions that the Court found, while serious, were nonetheless simply incidental and not material to the EPA's risk assessment. In effect, even though the EPA behaved badly in preventing the research process, the end product of that process—the risk assessment—could nonetheless be legitimate. In order to resolve this issue the Court needed to determine whether "consultation with the representative group would have likely produced a different result" (Osteen, 1998, p. 38) And in order to determine this, the Court was required to examine the substance of the EPA's risk assessment. In effect, if the plaintiffs' claims about the quality of the EPA's risk assessment are true, namely that the assessment is arbitrary, capricious and unreasoned, then it follows that the plaintiffs' legally required participation in the research and assessment process would have made a substantive difference. As Judge Osteen noted, the first issue

> is whether [the] EPA's consulting a representative com-
> mittee, on which industry's concerns were represented
> during the research process, likely would have caused
> [the] EPA to change the conduct or conclusions of its
> ETS assessment. The key to this determination is
> whether industry representatives could have presented
> meritable criticism and advice. (Osteen, 1998, p. 43)

What then of the industry's criticism of the EPA's ETS science: was it meritable?

The credibility of the EPA's risk assessment centers on three types of claims: first, about the biological plausibility of equating MS with ETS; second, about the epidemiological evidence regarding the health effects of ETS; and third, about the EPA's epidemiological methodology.

The EPA's biological plausibility thesis

The EPA's biological plausibility thesis is crucial to its risk assessment since it establishes an indispensable chain of argument. This runs as follows: first, the biological plausibility of equating MS with ETS justifies the EPA's *a priori* hypothesis that ETS is a Group A carcinogen; second, this hypothesis justifies the EPA's use of one-tailed significance tests and the rejection of negative findings; and third, the use of one-tailed significance tests leads to the use of 90 percent as opposed to 95 percent confidence levels. As the Court noted, "these issues are more than [sic] periphery. If [the] EPA's *a priori* hypothesis fails, [the] EPA has no justification for manipulating the Agency's standard scientific methodology" (Osteen, 1998, p. 65). Thus, if the biological plausibility argument is without merit, the entire risk assessment is seriously imperilled.

The plaintiffs raised three objections against the bioplausibility thesis, saying:

> [1) the EPA] ignored Assessment findings about the
> differences between MS and ETS; 2) [the] EPA ignored
> evidence rejecting any chemical similarity; and 3)
> [the] EPA did not define the criteria used to reach
> conclusions about the similarity / dissimilarity / in-
> determinacy of MS and ETS. (Osteen, 1998, p. 45)

The plaintiff's claims here were supported to a large extent both by the assessment and by prior EPA risk classifications. For instance, in chapter 4 of its report the EPA noted that "the rapid dilution of both SS and exhaled MS into the environment and changing phase distributions of ETS components over time raise some questions about the carcinogenic potential of ETS under actual environmental exposure conditions"

(Osteen, 1998, pp. 46-7). Again, the assessment record notes that the primary author of chapters 5 and 6, Kenneth Brown, argues that there "are differences between active and passive smoking that may affect carcinogenic risk that are not fully understood" (Osteen, 1998, pp. 46-7). Clearly the assessment's own authors appear to doubt the bioplausibility thesis. These doubts are also shared by others, and the plaintiffs introduced evidence citing scientific literature which also rejected the bioplausibility hypothesis.

Finally, there is an absence of any defined criteria as to how the chemical similarity of MS and ETS was established. This gives rise to the suspicion that the EPA changed its position on the alleged similarity of MS and ETS depending on what sort of argument it was attempting to make. As Judge Osteen noted, "It is striking that MS and ETS were similar only where such a conclusion promoted finding ETS a carcinogen" (Osteen, 1998, p. 61). Indeed, this suspicion is given considerable credence by the fact that in previous risk assessments the "EPA did not classify agents in Group A because they contain the same constituents as other Group A carcinogens" (Osteen, 1998, p. 49).

In response to these arguments, the EPA claimed that the bioplausibility thesis is supported in three ways: first, since active smoking is a cause of lung cancer in humans, it is reasonable to assume that ETS is a cause of lung cancer in humans because ETS is chemically similar to MS; second, there is evidence that non-smokers who are exposed to ETS absorb and metabolize significant amounts of it; and third, laboratory tests have shown that ETS causes cancer in animals and damages DNA. The EPA also rejected the assertion that it failed to provide criteria for determining the similarity of MS and ETS, arguing that it set out four criteria. (Osteen, 1998, pp. 51-52,54)

Judge Osteen found each of these arguments to be unconvincing due to the fact that "there is limited evidence in the record supporting [the] EPA's final basis for its bioplausibility hypothesis" (Osteen, 1998, p. 57). In other words, whatever the *post hoc* explanations devised for purposes of litigation, the scientific record of the assessment process does not support the EPA's claims of bioplausibility. Indeed, as the Court notes, it is not simply that there is limited evidentiary basis in the record to support the EPA's thesis—there is also substantial evidence in the assessment record that contradicts the EPA's plausibility thesis.

For instance, the scientists on the IAQC's final review panel themselves expressed significant reservations about the similarity of MS and ETS. "The data in Chapter 3 'do not adequately support the conclusion that the two are chemically similar ... [T]he data that are in there, speaking as a chemist, they simply don't make the case ... [T]he data ... simply does not demonstrate that they are similar'" (Osteen, 1998, p. 62).

What was most disturbing to the Court was what might be called the convenience factor; the fact that the bioplausibility hypothesis was maintained in the assessment only when it served the purposes of the EPA in finding ETS a carcinogen, and was abandoned in other places. The EPA attempted to justify these inconsistencies in the record on the basis of both quantitative and qualitative components of risk assessment, but both these were completely rejected by the Court.

> Neither the Assessment [n]or the administrative record explains why physicochemical inquiries require a bifurcated analysis instead of a combined analysis as per the Guidelines, or why MS and ETS are similar for purposes of hazard identification, but not for purposes of quantitative risk assessments. (Osteen, 1998, p. 60)

Moreover, the claims about ETS causing cancer in laboratory animals did not support the EPA's hypothesis either, since the

> studies detected no evidence of lung cancer and the Assessment does not explain, nor does [the] EPA direct the court to any evidence within the record explaining how SS condensate demonstrates similarities between MS and ETS. (Osteen, 1998, pp. 57-8)

But it is not simply the convenience factor that disturbed the Court. There was also the issue of circularity. Sensing that the case against ETS could not be sustained on the basis of the bioplausibility thesis, the EPA sought to reinforce the thesis with epidemiological studies, claiming that the epidemiological evidence supported the bioplausibility thesis. This reasoning was patently circular in that the EPA's "logic" turns on the independent integrity of the bioplausibility argument. As the EPA used the bioplausiblity argument to relax the standards of statistical significance for the epidemiological studies, it could hardly then use the contrived significance of those studies to justify bioplausibility. In short the biopausibility thesis was being asked to do too much. It could not both justify a manipulation of the epidemiological data and derive its support from that same data.

> The court is disturbed that [the] EPA and Kenneth Brown buttress the bioplausibility theory with the epidemiology studies. [The] EPA's theory must be independently plausible. [The] EPA relied upon similarities between MS and ETS to conclude that it is biologically plausible that ETS causes cancer. [The] EPA terms this theory its *"a priori* hypothesis" in justifying Chapter 5's methodology. Chapter 5's methodology allowed [the] EPA to demonstrate a sta-

> tistically significant association between ETS exposure
> and lung cancer ... Chapter 5's analysis rests on the
> validity of the biological plausibility there. It is circular
> for [the] EPA to now argue that epidemiology studies
> support the Agency's *a priori* theory. Without the the-
> ory, the studies would likely have done no such thing.
> (Osteen, 1998, p. 58)

What emerges from the both the assessment record and the litiga-
tive record on bioplausibility is a second pattern of corrupt science.
Consider the Court's conclusions:

> The court is faced with the ugly possibility that [the]
> EPA adopted a methodology for each chapter, without
> explanation, based on the outcome sought in that chap-
> ter. This possibility is most potent where [the] EPA
> rejected MS-ETS similarities to avoid a "cigarette-
> equivalents" analysis in determining carcinogenicity of
> ETS exposure. Use of cigarette-equivalents analysis
> may have lead to a conclusion that ETS is not a Group
> A carcinogen. (Osteen, 1998, p. 60)

> [The] EPA's assertion that "[it] did explain the numer-
> ous criteria it used in assessing similarity ... " is without
> merit. [The] EPA merely parrots the findings made in
> Chapter 3 of the ETS risk Assessment. The record pre-
> sents no evidence of [the] EPA establishing similarity
> criteria before the Assessment. (Osteen, 1998, p. 61)

> The record does not support [the] EPA's arguments
> that [it] took MS-ETS differences into account and,
> despite them, concluded ETS is a known human car-
> cinogen because nonsmokers are exposed to and
> absorb carcinogens. [The] EPA conceded that dilution,
> aging and exposure characteristics fundamentally dis-
> tinguish ETS from mainstream smoke, and "raise ...
> questions about the carcinogenic potential of ETS."...
> The record does not explain how, after raising these
> questions, [the] EPA could classify ETS a known hu-
> man carcinogen based on similarities between SS and
> MS. (Osteen, 1998, p. 63)

> The court is disturbed that [the] EPA and Kenneth
> Brown buttress the bioplausibility theory with the
> epidemiology studies. [The] EPA's theory must be in-
> dependently plausible ... It is circular for [the] EPA to
> now argue the epidemiology studies support the

> Agency's *a priori* theory. Without the theory, the stud-
> ies would have done no such thing. (Osteen, 1998,
> p. 58)

> If confronted by a representative committee that voiced
> industry concerns, [the] EPA would likely have had to
> resolve these issues in the record. It is not clear whether
> [the] EPA could have or can do so. These issues are
> more than [sic] periphery. If [the] EPA's *a priori* hy-
> pothesis fails, [the] EPA has no justification for
> manipulating the Agency's standard scientific method-
> ology. (Osteen, 1998, p. 65)

What is most striking about the Court's language is the repeated use of phrases like "the record presents no evidence", the "record does not explain how", and the "EPA's assertion is without merit", all of which point to the unreasoned, unscientific character of the EPA's bioplausi-bility hypothesis. Now it might be argued that the Court's language and analysis point to nothing more disturbing than incompetent science, that there is nothing here that rises to the level of corrupt science. While the process of the assessment might be corrupt, the substance of the assessment's science is merely incompetent, not corrupt.

Though in some senses appealing, this interpretation of the EPA's science is untenable for three reasons. First, the convenience factor is a clear mark of corrupt science. Rather than taking a consistent position about the alleged MS-ETS similarities, the EPA crafted positions de-pending on the required outcomes of a particular chapter in its report. Rather than basing its MS-ETS equivalency on some chemical basis, the EPA founded it instead on a pre-conceived policy outcome: namely, that ETS causes cancer in humans. Despite the contrived explanations of-fered to the Court, the only way in which the contradictory claims about MS-ETS similarities make any sense is within the pre-determined posi-tion of finding ETS a carcinogen. And this is without question the defining characteristic of corrupt science—mandated conclusion driving scientific explanation. In effect, Judge Osteen had discovered that the bioplausibility hypothesis was a pseudo-scientific front protecting a scientifically unjustified position, hence his reference to the "ugly pos-sibility."

Second, the circularity of the bioplausibility and epidemiological arguments and the EPA's tenacious defense of their interconnection is unlikely to be the product of mere incompetence. The logical unaccepta-bility of such reasoning is obvious to anyone operating at the EPA's level of policy and scientific sophistication. The EPA is clearly aware of the fact that it can only sustain its carcinogenicity finding through the bioplausiblity thesis; it is clearly aware of the fact that its bioplausibility thesis provides the rationale for manipulating the statistical outcomes of the epidemiological evidence; and it is clearly aware of the fact that it claims the bioplausiblity thesis is in turn supported by the manipulated epidemiological evidence. If the argumentative circle were less tight the circularity might be less apparent. But to characterize such openly illogical and manipulative practices as the product of inadvertence or incompetence is to ascribe to the EPA a level of inconceivable methodological schizophrenia.

Third, the consistent willingness of the EPA during the trial to misrepresent its positions, its evidence, and its reasoning on bioplausibility to the Court, together with its apparent unconcern with tortured and clearly untenable explanations, distinguishes its actions from the simply incompetent. Even the persistent language of the Court ("the record does not explain how", the "EPA's assertion is without merit") indicates a polite disdain for the Agency's contorted defense of its insupportable assertions. To take but one example, despite the Agency's claims that criteria for MS-ETS had been established prior to the assessment, there is no evidence of such a criteria having existed. Indeed, as the Court noted, no such criteria were presented at the IAQC final review panel, where the panel's neutral scientists raised fundamental and unanswered questions about the chemical similarity of MS and ETS. Thus, even allowing for the significant gaps in the assessment record, what record there is is at odds with the EPA's central hypothesis.

A similar instance of significant non-confirming evidence being completely ignored was the review of the EPA's own Risk Criteria Office, which recommended against the approach taken in the assessment (Osteen, 1998, p. 64). As the Court finally concluded, it is apparent that the arguments submitted during litigation do not represent the argumentative process or position developed during the assessment. Rather they are fundamentally misrepresentations designed to make the unreasonable look reasonable, "*post hoc* rationalizations devised during litigation" (Osteen, 1998, p. 73).

What the evidence shows, therefore, is that the EPA report was the result of corrupt science. Not only were the EPA's processes corrupt, but its evidence for and arguments about bioplausibility, or perhaps more appropriately lack of evidence, display a pattern of corruption.

The EPA's epidemiological evidence

The second issue on which the validity of the EPA's ETS assessment turns is the extent of the epidemiological evidence that the EPA examined. By the time that the EPA risk assessment appeared, there were 58 studies that examined the risks of lung cancer in ETS-exposed populations. Of these, 33 looked at the lung cancer risk of non-smoking females married to male smokers, and of these 33 the EPA based its assessment on 31 studies that were available at the time that it conducted its second IAQC review. One of the 31 studies was not ready in its complete form so the Agency used interim results only. In order to draw conclusions from all of the studies, the EPA submitted them to meta-analysis.

Given that the EPA based its analysis on only 31 of the available 58 studies it is worth noting which studies were excluded and why. The excluded studies fell into three groups: twelve studies examined the cancer risks of females exposed to ETS in the workplace; thirteen looked at cancer risks of females exposed to ETS during childhood; and two looked at cancer risks of females married to smokers. The EPA is remarkably silent as to why these 27 studies were excluded, the assessment noting only that more were included than excluded.

Now the EPA's IAQC noted that one of the conditions necessary for meta-analysis is a "precise definition of criteria used to include (or exclude) studies" (Osteen, 1998, p. 67). But it is clear from the assessment record that the EPA undertook the meta-analysis in the absence of any articulated criteria as to which studies to include. As the IQAC observed,

> [s]pecific criteria for including studies was not provided. The importance of this was reinforced at the Committee meeting when a re-analysis was presented on a different set of studies than those in the report. This resulted in a change in the overall risk estimate. Decisions as to study inclusion should be made prior to analysis, based on clearly stated criteria. (Osteen, 1998, p. 67)

The importance of having criteria is thus twofold. On the one hand, it is necessary for the validity of the meta-analysis because it forces a clear examination of the differences and similarities in the data which are being combined. On the other hand, it provides an important procedural element of transparency by certifying that the database is not biased towards some pre-determined outcome. This last requirement is particularly important in this case, as the EPA had already committed to a conclusion about ETS before it began its risk assessment. If the Agency cared at all about scientific and policy integrity it would have taken exceptional care in this phase of its assessment to conform to the process requirements outlined as necessary by its own IAQC.

But it did not. As the plaintiffs noted, this failure to create criteria and the consequent unexplained exclusion of important epidemiological data provides strong evidence of arbitrary, unreasoned decision-making.

> [The] Plaintiffs contest that [the] EPA excluded studies
> and data on workplace and childhood exposure to ETS,
> as well as the "two largest and most recent" U.S. spousal
> smoking studies, because inclusion would have under-
> mined [the] EPA's claim of a causal association
> between ETS exposure and lung cancer. (Osteen, 1998,
> p. 68)

In an attempt to deny the claim of arbitrariness designed to insure
a pre-determined outcome to the assessment, the EPA offered the Court
five post hoc reasons for excluding these 27 studies and including the
remaining 31. First, the data in the childhood and workplace studies
were said to be "less extensive and therefore less reliable" (Osteen, 1998,
p. 68). The Court noted that the EPA's evidence for this claim was
unconvincing both on the question of extent and reliability (Osteen,
1998, pp. 68-69).

Second, the EPA argued that the workplace studies were excluded
because of potential confounders. Again, the Court found no support in
the record for this claim. Third, the EPA explained that workplace
studies were excluded because most did not classify subjects by the
amount of their exposure. Here as well, the Court noted that this
reasoning was not part of the assessment record. Fourth, the EPA
claimed that the childhood studies were excluded because they were
founded on distant and perhaps unreliable memories and represented
a more limited exposure than spousal exposure. (Osteen, 1998, p. 70)
But, as the Court noted, there is nothing in the record to support the
claim that "childhood exposure data should be ignored" (Osteen, 1998,
p. 70). Again, the record does not reveal that the EPA used reliability of
memory of total lifetime exposure as a selection criterion. Indeed, if
memory reliability were to be used as a criterion, many of the studies
would have to be excluded, as all rely to some extent on recollection.

Fifth, regarding the spousal studies completed after the comment
period had passed and the EPA already had a considerable database;
the Agency justified its use of preliminary data from only one of the
three studies (the Fontham study) on the grounds it was the largest U.S.
ETS study and used methodology superior to any other study (Osteen,
1998, p. 71). These claims however, were again not supported by the
record. As the EPA failed to create criteria by which to select studies, it
could hardly claim that the Fontham study's methodology was superior: for, without criteria in which the weight given to methodology is
clearly articulated, such a claim appears to be nothing more than another explanation designed purely for the purposes of litigation. Indeed,
as Judge Osteen noted, given that there was no record of the methodol-

ogy employed in the other two studies, it would be impossible even to compare methodologies (Osteen, 1998, p. 71).

This returns us to the critical influence of the EPA's process violations on its substantive conclusions. With the open, representative process required by law and a full deliberative record, the EPA would have found it virtually impossible to be arbitrary, and indeed even to appear arbitrary. Disputes about criteria and study selection against that criteria would be answerable at least in principle. As Judge Osteen noted:

> In making a study choice, consultation with an advisory committee voicing these concerns would have resulted, at a minimum, in a record that explained [the] EPA's selective use of available information. From such a record, a reviewing court could then determine whether [the] EPA cherry-picked its data, and whether [the] EPA exceeded its statutory authority.
>
> [The] EPA's study selection is disturbing. First there is evidence in the record supporting the accusation that the EPA cherry-picked its data. Without criteria for pooling studies into a meta-analysis, the Court cannot determine whether the exclusion of studies likely to disprove [the] EPA's *a priori* hypothesis was coincidence or intentional. (pp. 72-73)

Of course, even allowing the EPA the benefit of the doubt about its motives does not clear it of other failures. By excluding nearly half of the available studies, the EPA failed to follow its own risk assessment guidelines, and contravened the Radon Research Act. The Act states that the EPA should gather data and information on all aspects of indoor air quality, while the Agency chose to selectively ignore significant amounts of data.

> [The] EPA's excluding nearly half of the available studies directly conflicts with [the] EPA's proposed purpose for analyzing the epidemiological studies and conflicts with the EPA's Risk Assessment Guidelines. [Further the] EPA's selective use of data conflicts with the Radon Research Act. The Act states [that the] EPA's program shall "gather data and information on *all aspects* of indoor air quality." In conducting a risk assessment under the Act, the EPA deliberately refused to assess information aspects of indoor air quality.
>
> At the outset, the court concluded risk assessments incidental to collecting information and making find-

> ings. [The] EPA steps outside the court's analysis when
> information collection becomes incidental to conduct-
> ing a risk assessment. (pp. 72-73)

In the absence of both a process ensuring objectivity and fairness, and criteria for methodological soundness, it is difficult not to conclude that the EPA's insistence on including the Fontham study was based less on reasoned decision-making than on its desire to support its *a priori* conclusion about ETS. Without the Fontham study, the epidemiological evidence would not have produced the desired conclusion. Further, including all three of the large US studies along with the workplace and childhood exposure studies would have made the EPA's carcinogen classification of ETS impossible. Hence, the Court's observation that, for the EPA, examining the evidence and information collection became incidental to conducting a risk assessment (Osteen, 1998, p. 72-73).

But is this assessment of the EPA's methods and motivation too harsh? Consider the following scenario. You announce a scientific con-clusion prior to examining the scientific evidence supporting that conclusion. Upon examining the scientific evidence you find that the bulk of the evidence, in this case epidemiological studies, does not support your conclusion. You now have two options: one, to withdraw or modify your conclusion; two, to adjust the evidence to support your conclusion. You decide to maintain your conclusion. This means that the embarrassing counter-evidence must be dealt with. To do this you create, off the record, two classes of evidence, evidence that is helpful to your conclusion and evidence that is unhelpful to your conclusion.

Evidence that is unhelpful to your conclusion is not used; evidence that is helpful becomes the foundation of your case. When asked later to explain why certain pieces of evidence were examined and became the basis of your conclusion, you put forward a series of explanations, none of which is supported by any evidence that they actually drove your original selection.

We would argue that what emerges from the Court record is just this scenario—a predetermined conclusion driving a selective process of evidence-gathering, in which the key to selection is not scientific integrity but support for one's pre-determined conclusion. It is this process in which, as Judge Osteen noted, evidence collection and exami-nation become incidental to truth-finding, that justifies the characterization of corrupt science.

The EPA's epidemiological methodology

The third and final issue upon which the validity of the EPA's ETS risk assessment hinges is the Agency's epidemiological methodology. The plaintiffs raised seven specific methodological issues, charging that the EPA deviated from accepted scientific procedure and its own risk assessment guidelines in a manner designed to ensure a pre-ordained outcome (Osteen, 1998, pp. 73-4). Despite the significant problems already identified with the assessment, however, Judge Osteen thought it unnecessary to delve further into what he called the EPA's epidemiological web. But there were two methodological issues so serious, and in which the EPA's conduct was so unjustified, that the Court considered they merited further examination.

The first of these issues was the question of confidence intervals. The plaintiffs alleged that, without explanation, the EPA switched from using standard 95 percent confidence intervals to 90 percent confidence intervals in order to enhance the likelihood that its meta-analysis would appear statistically significant. This shift assisted the EPA in obtaining statistically significant results that could be used to support a Group A classification (p. 74).

With a 95 percent confidence interval, there is only a 5 percent probability that the result—in this case that ETS causes lung cancer—is a product of chance. Generally, researchers are unwilling to accept higher probabilities of error. In its 1990 draft of the risk assessment, the EPA used a 95 percent interval, but in subsequent drafts they switched to a 90 percent confidence interval. This change was criticized by Geoffrey Kabat, who served on the IAQC and also contributed to the risk assessment. Kabat noted,

> The use of 90% confidence intervals, instead of the conventionally used 95% confidence intervals, is to be discouraged. It looks like an attempt to achieve statistical significance for a result which otherwise would not achieve significance. (Osteen, 1998, p. 75)

Why then, in the face of such internal criticism, would the EPA change its confidence intervals? In its risk assessment the EPA argued that this usage was justified by the *a priori* hypothesis that a positive association exists between exposure to ETS and lung cancer (Osteen, 1998, p. 75). But as noted earlier, this explanation fails because it is circular. In a second attempt, the EPA explained to the Court that use of the 95 percent confidence interval with the one-tailed test would have produced an apparent discrepancy: statistically significant study results using the standard p-value of .05 might nevertheless have a 95 percent confidence interval that included a relative risk of one (Osteen, 1998, pp. 75-76). In short, these studies would have failed to confirm that ETS was a significant health risk. As Judge Osteen observed:

> The record and [the] EPA's explanations to the Court make it clear that using standard methodology, [the] EPA could not produce statistically significant results with its selected studies. Analysis conducted with a .05 significance level and a 95% confidence level included relative risks of 1. Accordingly, these results did not confirm [the] EPA's controversial *a priori* hypothesis. In order to confirm its hypothesis, [the] EPA maintained its standard significance level but lowered the confidence interval to 90%. This allowed [the] EPA to confirm its hypothesis by finding a relative risk of 1.19, albeit a very weak association. (Osteen, 1998, p. 77)

What drove the EPA to change its confidence intervals and its epidemiological methodology is thus the same thing that drove it to select certain epidemiological studies in preference to other studies—the determination, regardless of the costs to scientific integrity and its statutory responsibilities, to justify its pre-determined position that ETS was a human carcinogen. Indeed, the record shows that even after carefully selecting its studies, the EPA still could not make its ETS case without abandoning normal scientific procedures. Again, the Court noted that the record does not provide any reason for the EPA's abandonment of the 95 percent confidence interval (p. 78), despite the Agency's clear responsibility to explain changes in methodology used during the conduct of a risk assessment. But the EPA can no more explain why it changed confidence intervals than it can explain anything else about its process and findings. To do so would be to admit to scientific corruption.

Further reason to believe that the EPA's science was corrupt is to be found in the Court's comments about the second problem with the EPA's epidemiological methodology. As a result of its statistical analysis using a 90 percent confidence interval, the EPA concluded that the relative risk (RR) of ETS was 1.19, and it was this finding that provided a large measure of its justification for the Group A classification (Osteen, 1998, p. 76). Yet, as the plaintiffs noted, the EPA failed to provide any reason why such a weak RR justified a Group A classification. Every other Group A carcinogen had been required to exhibit a much higher relative risk (Osteen, 1998, p. 76) and a recent candidate for Group A status with an RR range of between 2.6 and 3.0 had not been classified as a Group A carcinogen. Further, Dr. Kabat of the IAQC had noted that: "An association is generally considered weak if the odds ratio is under

3.0 and particularly when it is under 2.0, as is the case in the relationship of ETS and lung cancer" (Osteen, 1998, pp. 76-77).

Clearly then, there is no precedent for Group A classification on the basis of such a weak RR. But why should the issue of consistency, adherence to normal procedure and evidence-based decision-making be thought important at this final stage? Consider what had preceded this final step in the assessment process: certain epidemiological studies had been deemed relevant and others irrelevant on the basis of no clear criteria; the relevant epidemiological studies had been analyzed at a 90 percent confidence level rather than the usual 95 percent confidence level; and this in turn had produced a RR of 1.19, which in no other circumstance would be judged sufficient to justify Group A classification.

Two things about this process of scientific corruption were particularly troubling to the Court. First, and most obviously, with such a weak RR, the problems with study selection and methodology meant that the EPA could not show a statistically significant association between ETS and lung cancer in non-smokers (Osteen, 1998, p. 78). In other words, the risk assessment was invalid.

Second, while the Radon Act authorizes the EPA to collect information, conduct research and disseminate findings; the EPA's epidemiological basis for its risk assessment actually represented a suppression, if not a misrepresentation, of information. "[The] EPA did not disclose in the record or in the Assessment: its ability to demonstrate a statistically significant relationship under normal methodology; the reasoning behind adopting a one-tailed test, or that only after adjusting the Agency's methodology could a weak relative risk be demonstrated. Instead of disclosing information, the Agency withheld significant portions of its findings and reasoning in striving to confirm its *a priori* hypothesis" (Osteen, 1998, pp. 78-79).

As noted earlier, two of the most characteristic features of corrupt science are its misrepresentation of reality and its misrepresentation of its process. Rather than acknowledging alternative evidence, or problems with its evidence that would cast doubt on its conclusions, and rather than admitting the complexity of the issue under review and the limits of the evidence; corrupt science presents what is at best a carefully chosen half truth as the whole truth necessary for public policy. In effect, public policy is manipulated into reaching certain conclusions on the basis of data that have been fabricated, falsified, misrepresented, or massaged to appear in a guise fundamentally at odds with reality. Corrupt science misrepresents not only reality, but also its own processes in arriving at its conclusions. Instead of acknowledging the selectivity of its process and the official insistence to demonstrate a predetermined conclusion, corrupt science invests both its process and its conclusions with a mantle of indubitability.

This is precisely what the Court found in this case. The EPA failed to disclose its processes and its failure to make its case under normal scientific procedures. Is also failed to disclose its reasoning for changing its normal procedures, both methodological and with respect to the RR level required for Group A status. Most importantly, it failed to reveal how dependent its findings were on these departures from the norm. As a result, what the EPA presented as fact would be accepted by the casual observer as being scientifically supported, when in actuality the truth was fundamentally different.

Conclusion

Judge Osteen began his analysis of the EPA's risk assessment by asking whether a different process would have produced different results; in effect, asking whether the EPA's science was open to question. In his conclusion, he pulled together his findings both about the process and the substance of the EPA's risk assessment, to determine whether the risk assessment demonstrated reasoned decision making. He entered judgment in favour of the plaintiffs and vacated the EPA's ETS risk assessment. The Judge's major findings (Osteen, 1998) were:

1. In 1988, the EPA initiated drafting policy-based recommendations about controlling ETS exposure because the EPA believed ETS is a Group A carcinogen. (p. 87)

2. Rather than reach a conclusion after collecting information, researching, and making findings, the EPA categorized ETS as a known cause of cancer in 1989. (pp. 87-88)

3. The EPA determined it was biologically plausible that ETS causes lung cancer. In doing so, the EPA recognized problems with its theory, namely dissimilarities between MS and ETS. In other areas of the Assessment, the EPA relied on these dissimilarities in justifying its methodology. (p. 80)

4. The EPA did not explain much of the criteria and assertions upon which the EPA's theory relies. (p. 80)

5. The EPA claimed that selected epidemiologic studies would affirm its plausibility theory. The studies selected did not include a significant number of studies and data which demonstrated no association between ETS and cancer. (p. 80)

6. The EPA did not explain its criteria for study selection, thus leaving itself open to allegations of cherry picking. (pp. 80-81)

7. Using its normal methodology and its selected studies, the EPA did not demonstrate a statistically significant association between ETS and lung cancer. (p. 81)

8. This should have caused the EPA to re-evaluate the inference options used in establishing its plausibility theory. (p. 81)

9. The EPA then claimed the bioplausibility theory, renominated the *a priori* hypothesis, justified a more lenient methodology. (p. 88)

10. The EPA claimed, but did not explain how, its theory justified changing the Agency's methodology. (p. 81)

11. With a new technology, the EPA demonstrated from the selected studies a very low risk for lung cancer based on ETS exposure. Based on its original theory and the weak evidence of association, the EPA concluded the evidence showed a causal relationship between cancer and ETS. (pp. 88-89)

12. In conducting the ETS risk assessment, the EPA disregarded information and made findings on selective information and did not disseminate significant epidemiologic information deviated from its risk assessment guidelines; failed to disclose important findings and reasoning; and left significant questions without answers. The EPA's conduct left substantial holes in the administrative record. The EPA produced limited evidence, then claimed the weight of the Agency's research evidence demonstrated ETS causes cancer. (p. 90)

13. So long as information collection on all relevant aspects of indoor air quality, research and dissemination are the lodestars, the general language of the Radon Research Act authorizes risk assessments. (p. 89)

14. Gathering all relevant information, researching, and disseminating findings were subordinate to the EPA's demonstrating ETS as a Group A carcinogen. (p. 90)

15. In the Radon Research Act, Congress granted the EPA limited research authority along with an obligation to seek advice from a representative committee during such research. Congress intended for an industry representative to be at the table and their voice heard during the research process. The EPA's authority under the act is contingent upon the Agency hearing and responding to the represented constituents concerns. The recorded evidence is overwhelming that IAQC was not the representative body required under the Act. Had the EPA reconciled industry objections voiced from a representative body during the research process, the ETS risk

assessment would very possibly not have been conducted in the same manner nor reached the same conclusions. (p. 91)

But, to return to where we began, does the pattern of conduct described here consistently constitute corrupted science? We would argue that it does. Indeed, we would suggest that the EPA's ETS risk assessment is a case study in the corruption of science. Recall that corrupt science involves four characteristics: movement from policy to science rather than science to policy; misrepresentation of reality through misrepresentation of evidence; misrepresentation of processes; and attempts to suppress dissent through attacks on the character and motivation of dissent rather than on its logic and the evidence. The Court's findings are decisive in each of these areas.

Movement from policy to science The record clearly shows that the EPA began with a conclusion about ETS (points 1, 2, 14 above), rather than with a question. As the Court noted, the EPA's collection and assessment of evidence was merely incidental window-dressing to the process of conducting a risk assessment (pp. 72-73). Everything that the EPA did was designed to bring about the desired conclusion.

Misrepresentation of reality First, the EPA proposed a bioplausibility hypothesis which was insupportable, then sought to bolster the thesis with epidemiological evidence while simultaneously claiming that the same evidence supported bioplausibility (points 2, 3, 8, 9 above). Further, the EPA attempted to mislead the Court about the evidence for the bioplausibility thesis and its inconsistent use of the theory.

Second, rather than present the entire evidentiary record, the EPA arbitrarily excluded certain epidemiological studies which demonstrated no association between ETS and cancer (points 5, 6, 7, above). The EPA provided no credible reasons for its exclusion of certain studies and inclusion of other studies.

Third, having found that even its selected studies failed to demonstrate an association between ETS and lung cancer, the EPA re-analyzed its studies using a 90 percent confidence interval rather than a 95 percent interval. The Agency provided no explanation for its change in methodology. This allowed the Agency to demonstrate a statistically significant risk of lung cancer in non-smokers exposed to ETS (points 7, 9, 10, 11).

Fourth, the EPA used the resulting RR of 1.19 as the major basis for its Group A classification of ETS, despite the fact that every other Group A carcinogen had required a higher RR and despite the fact that its own IAQC member Dr. Kabat indicated that a RR of 1.19 indicated a weak association. The EPA failed to provide the Court with convincing reasons for this inconsistency (points 10, 11, 12).

Fifth, the EPA failed to disclose its inability to demonstrate statistical significance under normal scientific procedures and the fact that its weak RRs were obtained only after changing methodology. Indeed, the Agency withheld significant portions of its findings and reasoning (p. 79) (points 12, 13).

Misrepresenting its processes First, the EPA failed to conform to the procedural requirements of the Radon Act, requirements that were designed to create an objective and transparent process of risk assessment in which all sides had the opportunity, on the record, to examine the evidence (point 15). Further, the EPA attempted to maintain that it had discharged its procedural responsibilities for openness and objectivity through the IAQC, despite the fact that the IAQC contained no industry representation, and that its concerns on several points were ignored by the Agency.

Second, the EPA's risk assessment failed to disclose the nature of its scientific process, namely, that it moved from conclusion to evidence rather than from evidence to conclusion, and that everything was subordinate to demonstrating that ETS was a Group A carcinogen (p. 90) (points 1, 2, 14).

Third, the EPA's risk assessment process failed to provide a record of the rationale for its decisions to ignore the criticisms and reservations of its own Risk Criteria Office and IAQC members, its decisions about its data selection, its decisions about epidemiological methodology, and its decisions about Group A status in the presence of a weak association. In the absence of such a record it is impossible to conclude whether the EPA acted rationally (points 12, 15).

Fourth, the EPA failed to reveal the circular argumentative process involved with the bioplausibility thesis, the arbitrary process of its data selection, and the methodological departures from standard scientific practice (points 7, 10, 11, 12)

Suppressing dissent First, the EPA viewed the tobacco industry's scientific positions as untenable, not on the basis of evidence or logic, but simply because they were advanced by the industry. As industry attorney Rupp's letter indicated, at no time was there an opportunity for a scientific discussion of the fundamental issues regarding ETS (Kluger, 1996, p. 10). The EPA's attitude to the legitimacy of the industry's science is neatly captured in the reply of an assistant EPA administrator, William Rosenberg, to Rupp: "Frankly, the tobacco industry's argument would be more credible if it were not so similar to the tobacco industry's position on direct smoking" (Kluger, 1996, p. 693).

Second, the EPA's certainty about ETS, in advance of the evidence, created such a belief in the unfalsifiability of its *a priori* hypothesis that it apparently encouraged a climate in which even members of its own advisory panel like Dr. Geoffrey Kabat, who disagreed with its processes and conclusions, were challenged not on the basis of their scientific arguments but on their alleged and in fact non-existent connection to the tobacco industry. As Jacob Sullum writes, "In this context anyone who questioned the case against ETS risked being portrayed as a tool of the cigarette companies—even if, like Kabat, he had never received a dime from them" (Sullum, p. 172). Inasmuch as the a priori hypothesis was a revealed dogma, dissent could have no legitimate foundation. Character, not coherence and consistency, was the criteria against which disagreements were measured.

Thus, the case for corrupt science is compelling. Each of the characteristics of corrupt science is present in multiple instances, wound together within a consistent pattern. It would be difficult indeed to provide an alternative account which provides so coherent an explanation for so many of the uncontested facts of the case.

Chapter Five

The Consequences
of Corrupted Science

Introduction

The immediately visible effects of the EPA risk assessment are difficult to miss. In the six years since the assessment appeared, the United States has increasingly become a society in which public smoking is both legally and morally proscribed. In fact, the change in perception about the acceptability of smoking in public places (and, for some, in private places as well) is much more dramatic than the change in perception about smoking brought about by the first Surgeon General's report over three decades ago. Thousands of ordinances have been passed at the state and local levels that have either sharply restricted public smoking or banned it completely. Thousands of employers have similarly restricted or eliminated smoking in the workplace. And, most importantly, the overwhelming majority of Americans now believe that second-hand tobacco smoke is a threat to their health. It is this belief about the consequences of other people's tobacco smoke that is most significant, for it has brought about a fundamental change in the way in which individuals think about the morality of smoking–both their own and others.

For most of the twentieth century the campaign to de-legitimize smoking has employed two major weapons, science and morality. Though the mix has varied, the conjunction of the two has been consistent and highly effective. For example, once it was established that smoking increased the risks of ill-health in smokers, the groundwork was laid for a series of moral arguments that purported to show that subjecting oneself to these risks was both so irrational and so immoral as to justify government efforts to prevent one from assuming the risks. From this perspective the government was morally justified in intervening in the lives of adults to prevent them from making what the government believed to be a stupid decision, namely smoking.

But, however closely aligned to science, this sort of government paternalism, even in the interests of preventing smoking, was only minimally attractive. Indeed, in democratic societies like the United States, government intervention to protect competent adults from themselves—to coerce healthy lifestyles—always had a totalitarian flavor that ensured significant and widespread opposition.

The EPA's ETS risk assessment, however, changed this. With the "science" to show that smoking was not merely something that posed a risk to one's health, but also to the health of others, the campaign to outlaw smoking was able to change the moral character of the smoking debate. If the dangers of smoking went beyond the smoker to innocent bystanders then there were significant public consequences of smoking that justified policy measures to restrict, ban, or criminalize public smoking.

Public smoking was more than a disagreeable nuisance that annoyed non-smokers—it was now a certified health hazard to others. Smokers were no longer simply risk-taking fellow citizens but immoralists who imposed their risks on others. The EPA's ETS assessment though without regulatory effect, achieved regulatory ends through the effective use of "science" to change the moral status of smoking. The widespread prohibitions of public smoking derive their ultimate legitimacy from the belief that ETS causes cancer, which in turn drives the moral belief that public smoking is wrong. In this case what the law says, that smoking in public is illegal, and what morality says, smoking in public is wrong, are completely complementary.

The EPA's work, however, has been more than a domestic success: it has also established a brisk export market for US smoking "science" and regulation. Governments as close to hand as Canada and as far away as Hong Kong have invoked the EPA's assessment as the basis for their own varieties of anti-smoking legislation. Australia, for instance, used the work of the EPA as a cornerstone of its own "scientific" report on the health effects of passive smoking (Luik, 1996). Indeed, so fundamental to the crusade against smoking has the EPA report become that almost any public policy measure against smoking, whether about advertising, access, education or taxation, justifies itself by citing the dangers to public health of other people's tobacco smoke.

Corrupted science and society: the moral issues

For the EPA and the anti-smoking movement, the consequences of the risk assessment have been morally unambiguous. Both science and morality have condemned smoking and there is precious little moral space that the defenders of smoking can safely inhabit. But should this be the case? The EPA's assessment, which we have argued represents a case study in corrupt science, has been voided after judicial review, and the moral issues involved are much less clear than popularly believed. Indeed, the scientific corruption inherent in the process and substance of the EPA's risk assessment has raised several fundamentally disturbing issues.

The first of these is the question of the legitimacy of official misrepresentation, for corrupted science is at bottom science that misrepresents the state of reality. It is important to note the word official: the EPA was acting neither as a private scientist nor as a group of scientists representing some commercial interest. Rather, it was acting in its official capacity as a government agency, speaking about science on behalf of the government to fellow citizens as well as to fellow scientists.

The record notes that it was not speaking the truth. What the Court record shows is a profound and systematic disregard for the truth about ETS. Not only does the record reveal data manipulation to produce the desired policy outcome and data suppression or dismissal when it contradicted that outcome; it shows mandated policy processes not being followed, usual scientific practices (about criteria-setting for meta-analysis and confidence levels) being changed arbitrarily, and the absence of justification for these actions. The result is that anyone, scientist or citizen, who reads the report without the benefit of the Court's decision would be led to believe that legitimate science was at work, and to trust in its results. But then that is precisely what corrupt science is designed to do—misrepresent reality convincingly. The EPA's imprimatur is designed to reassure, to say in effect: "Legitimate science is at work here. You can be confident about the results."

If one digs a bit deeper what one recognizes is an ethic that legitimizes misrepresentation in the service of a good cause, a smoke-free society. Its antecedents are various but it most famous modern exponent is Marc Lalonde, the former Canadian Health minister, who argued that while doubts and uncertainties were fine in research science, when it comes to modifying the behaviour of the population such doubts were inappropriate. In the public health arena, science must speak with certainty, with no trace of ambiguity or discord lest it provide the excuse needed by many to cultivate and tolerate an environment and lifestyle that is hazardous to health. This position is generally referred to as the Lalonde Doctrine (Lalonde, 1974).

So common has this sort of argument become that it now appears to be the official ethic of the public health movement. Consider, for instance, the words of Professor John Last in his plenary address to the International Epidemiological Association.

> Another kind of credibility is more worrying. This is
> rigid, insensitive application of scientific rigor that dis-

regards the weight of circumstantial evidence, calling
into question the validity of epidemiological findings
when it is not in the public interest to do so. (Last, 1994)

Indeed, the EPA's ETS work seems to be a perfect instance of
Professor Last's comments being taken seriously, as no one could rightly
charge it with a scientific rigor that disregards the weight of circumstantial evidence.

At bottom then, the EPA's resort to corrupt science appears to have
legitimized official scientific misrepresentation as long as such misrepresentation is done from the allegedly pure motives of promoting public
health. Public smoking has become illegitimate through legitimizing
scientific misconduct. This might be called an instance of the contain-
ment theory: honourable intentions build a strong enough wall around
the dirty business of lying that the lying can never break out and become
institutionalized. The frightening thing about such deceit, however, is
that it is both so easy to justify and so difficult to restrict its use to the
ends that originally justified its employment. How, for instance, are we
to know when it is that the EPA or other government scientific agencies
are telling us the truth as opposed to lying to us for allegedly justifiable
reasons? How too, are we to be certain that this culture of misrepresentation and its methods of dissimulation will not spread beyond their
good uses to uses less desirable? How will we be certain that people and
processes, once corrupted, will not be so taken with the easy policy
dominance that it provides that they will be unwilling to return to the
hard work of real science?

Equally important are the implications for trust once such lying for
"noble" ends is exposed. The busy and scientifically unlettered public
depends on the government to provide it with truthful scientific information about health risks. If a major piece of scientific information
presented as true by the government is later found to be false, the
public's confidence in the government's ability and willingness to provide truthful information is significantly undermined. At the very least
the public comes to have doubts about the credibility of subsequent
government scientific information; at the very most citizens come to
view as tainted and untrustworthy all scientific claims advanced by
government.

But there is a second moral question here that goes beyond the
morality of official scientific misrepresentation. This is what might be
called the morality of suppressing dissent. Both the institutional processes of producing corrupted science and of utilizing it as a basis for
public policy demand a fundamental intolerance of dissent, both at the
scientific and the policy level. The imperatives of public health promotion which so effectively, though questionably, justify

misrepresentation, allow no place for the ambiguities and uncertainties that form a legitimate part of science, nor for the usual questions about the nature and quality of the evidence and whether it justifies a public policy response. This means that scientific and policy dissent must be suppressed through characterizing dissenters as either in the pay of the tobacco industry or at the margins of the scientific and public policy establishment, a strategy that in itself raises a host of subsidiary moral questions. As Jacob Sullum observes about the EPA's assessment process:

> Then, too, expressing skepticism about the case against ETS can be risky. "The tobacco industry for decades sort of denied the findings of epidemiologists, even though they are incredibly strong," Enstrom says. "Now it's like you can't agree with anything that the tobacco industry says, even if there might actually be some truth in it." He remembers receiving phone calls in 1994 from people who had seen his comments on ETS quoted in the press. The gist of their complaint was, "How can you possibly say something like that? It can be misused." Gough recalls that after he publicly doubted that ETS causes lung cancer, Representative Henry Waxman, sponsor of the Smoke-Free Environment Act, wrote "very strong letters to the director of the OTA, saying, 'What is Gough doing here?'"
>
> Members of the EPA's advisory panel were not immune to such pressures. In November 1990 the Associated Press (AP) reported that six of the sixteen panelists, including its chairman, had ties to a tobacco industry research group. The AP was referring to the Center for Indoor Air Research, which is funded mainly by tobacco companies. Five of the panelists had advised or reviewed research proposals for the center, while a sixth had received one of its grants. The story added that a seventh panelist, Geoffrey Kabat, had been recommended by Philip Morris ... In a subsequent editorial, entitled "Objectivity Up in Smoke," the *New York Times* questioned the credibility of all seven scientists and recommended that the panel be reconstituted ...
>
> In this context anyone who questioned the case against ETS risked being portrayed as a tool of the cigarette companies—even if, like Kabat, he had never received a dime from them. "Painting people in this

way reminds you of, 'Were you ever a member of the
Communist Party?'" Kabat says: "I felt really put on the
spot, because I did not want to be seen as a spokesman,
giving grist to the tobacco lobby's mill. But I also felt
that I had an ethical obligation to not let pass the kind
of stuff that was going on ... In a way, it was a political
game. It wasn't primarily about science." (Sullum, 1998,
pp. 171-2)

Geoffrey Kabat was taking a moral stand in a institutional climate
and process in which dissent was seen as an act of immorality. Whatever
the cost, "science" must be seen to provide a conclusive and united
answer to the question of ETS. There simply is no room in such a process
for people like Kabat. Despite the vital role in science of questions,
argument and dissent, these have no place in the corrupted world of the
EPA ETS science.

The third and by far the most morally objectionable consequence of
the EPA's corrupted science is its use by the anti-smoking movement to
deprive smokers not only of their right to pursue their pleasure in
public, but quite possibly to gain or retain their employment or advance
their prospects. Put in its bluntest fashion it is the issue of the moral
justification of using corrupted science to hurt innocent people. For it is
vital to remember that since the EPA report does not demonstrate a
significant risk to non-smokers, smokers cannot be accused of posing a
significant threat to non-smokers. They may be a source of annoyance,
but annoyance is not at all on the same moral plane as harm to others.
Without the "harm to others" argument, smoking becomes once again a
self-regarding behaviour, interventions against which can only be advanced on patently paternalistic grounds.

The moral offense here is thus one in which the innocent are
harmed, sometimes in quite significant ways, on the basis of corrupt
science and for no good reason. What makes the morality of the EPA's
assessment as corrupt as its science is that it seems prepared to deliberately create false concerns about ETS in order to exploit society's
willingness to curtail human rights in the interest of public health. In
doing this, the EPA's assessment sets in motion a process which simultaneously violates two fundamental moral principles: first, it treats
persons, in this case smokers and their alleged harm to others, as simply
means to the end of a smoke-free society and not as an end in their own
right; and second, by inflicting substantial pain on an entire class of
people—smokers—without their consent and for no justified reason.

But the question of the moral justifiability of using corrupted science
to hurt people goes beyond the question of depriving individuals of
their right to something they like (smoking in public, or even a job) to

something far more crucial, namely, the justifiability of depriving people of their moral standing through stigmatizing them as moral outcasts. In the end, of course, this is the logical outcome of the EPA's corrupt ETS science—to have their depiction of smokers as moral miscreants accepted by everyone, smokers included. From the beginning, corrupt ETS science had two key audiences: one the non-smoking majority who are intended to fear and hate smokers, and the other the smoking minority whose newly awakened self-loathing is designed to provide the seed bed of behavioral reform. It is indeed but a short logical and moral step from the claim "breathing someone else's tobacco smoke kills" to "smokers kill."

Surely there is nothing more morally loathsome than to corrupt science for the purposes of manipulating not only public policy but the public's beliefs about family, friends, and workmates so as to create a class of citizens who come to despise themselves for what they mistakenly believe they do to others and who in turn are despised by their fellow citizens for allegedly threatening their well-being. The ultimate moral consequence of the EPA's assessment is to foster a climate of distrust and disrespect in which the normal standards of respect and tolerance that make community life possible are significantly eroded. Corrupt science here is deliberately designed to fashion a society which believes that smokers are thoughtless menaces to the health of their fellow citizens, and who by their behaviour place themselves on the periphery of the moral community, if not outside it.

At the end of the day the assessment's corrupt science poses a threat to that most fragile aspect of social capital: trust. To the extent that its evidence is shown to be contrived or disconnected from its conclusions, it lessens every thoughtful citizen's trust and respect for both science and government. To the extent that it misrepresents reality through creating a risk where none exists, it makes non-smokers distrustful of smokers and smokers distrustful of themselves.

Corrupted science and society: the public policy issues

We have argued that the moral consequences for society of the EPA's corrupt ETS science are substantial. Unfortunately, the effects are not simply confined to the larger issues of society but also resonate within the more limited public policy sphere. We wish to examine six specific consequences for democratic public policy.

The operative word here is, of course, democratic. We are not concerned with the uses of bad science in non-democratic societies. In fact, with the appropriate degree of space we might wish to argue that non-democratic societies, or more specifically totalitarian societies, might be peculiarly receptive to the use of corrupted science. Our concern here, however, is with the effects of using corrupted since as a mechanism for framing, debating and justifying democratic public policy. Our principal claim is that the use of such science creates a climate which is fundamentally at odds with the character of democratic public policy and democratic society. Indeed, it might be the case that the consistent use of such science will in time significantly weaken the character of any democratic society.

The easiest way to understand the threat that corrupted science poses to democratic public policy and to democratic life as a whole is to understand what it is that democratic public policy attempts to do. Though its purposes are numerous and there is genuine debate about whether they ought to be broadly expansive or tightly constrained, there is probably a modest consensus that the general goal of democratic public policy is to minimize public harm, insofar as this is possible within the context of such foundational democratic values as diversity, autonomy, respect, rationality and fairness. These foundational values serve to place certain boundaries around what public policy can do, as well as define the minimal process requirements for how it ought to be done. They serve as both symbolic and conceptual reminders that in democratic communities there are certain things that are off-limits to the policy process. Let us characterize briefly five of these foundational values.

Diversity This is the recognition that people within a democratic society hold diverse beliefs and values, the rich complexity of which, more often than not, is not captured by the social science theories and data that are the tools of choice in the public policy process. This diversity, moreover, is simply not reflected in conflicting notions of what direction society should take, but more basically in differing pictures of what makes a good personal life. By accepting diversity as a foundational value, democratic society and the democratic public policy process accept it not just as a fact, but as something to be encouraged, enhanced, and celebrated as a strength.

Autonomy This is the recognition that, subject to the acceptance of certain minimal core values necessary for any society to exist, the individuals who make up democratic society are the best judges of the shape that they wish their lives to take. Therefore, they should be accorded the maximum liberty, compatible with similar liberty for everyone else, to think, believe, and live as they choose. This means that the state will resist the strong temptation, however well-intentioned, to misuse the public policy process to promote a single communal vision of the good life that excludes others.

Respect This is the recognition of the equality of human and moral standing with the state that the citizens of a democratic society possess. It is the recognition that the democratic state sees its citizens as persons of intrinsic worth, equivalent in dignity and standing with itself, with lives not to be managed or saved, but to be allowed to develop in ways of their own choosing. This means that the state's role should be to encourage its citizens to define themselves and their life-projects in widely varying ways, to foster the development of self-respect through deferring, to the greatest extent possible, from moral judgments about the self-definitions and life-projects of their citizens; and to create the conditions which allow its citizens lives the greatest possible chance of fulfillment.

Rationality This is the recognition that the activities of the state and the public policy process must be grounded in respect for the rational; that is, adherence to rational standards in the use of assumptions, the consideration of evidence, and methods of analysis. This commits government to processes and actions that are non-arbitrary and can withstand reasoned scrutiny. Processes and decisions must meet the minimal test of reasonableness through being clear, coherent and compelling. The evidence supporting public policy measures must be substantial, coherent, and reflective of reality; and the measures proposed must have a significant promise of being effective. At the same time the recognition of the value of rationality implies acceptance of the fact that truth is frequently complex and difficult to discover. Reality will often be richer and denser than evidence and theories. Though some problems will not have easily identifiable causes and solutions, this does not justify public policy formulated in the absence of reason and on the basis of surmises, hunches or appeals to intuition.

Fairness This is the recognition that democracy entails a foundational commitment to equal openness and access. It is the recognition of the importance, within an objective and non-arbitrary framework, of eliciting, examining and considering the views of all those whose legitimate interests are likely to be affected by collective decision-making. It is the recognition that power within a democratic society will not be exercised through processes that preclude the statement and examination of certain perspectives.

What these values suggest is that both the agenda of legitimate public policy and the process used to argue about that agenda are constrained by certain non-negotiable values. What marks out certain policy options and certain policy processes as illegitimate and non-democratic is their conflict with these core non-negotiable values.

For example, a public policy which significantly undermined autonomy, or tended to eliminate diversity and tolerance, or failed to consider divergent points of view fairly, or used poor argument or flawed evidence to advance policy options, would fail to qualify as legitimate democratic public policy because it conflicted with one or more of the key values on which democratic public policy and democracy itself are founded.

Placed within this context it is clear that the EPA's ETS assessment is a threat to the very core of democratic values and democratic public policy. The use of corrupt science in the policy creation process threatens each of the values (diversity, autonomy, respect, rationality and fairness) that are foundational to democracy. And this is something that should concern every citizen, smoker and non-smoker alike.

The first threat to democratic public policy that arises from the EPA's process of corrupt science is the threat to science's main virtue in the public policy process—its objectivity. Indeed, without science's objectivity, science loses its privileged position in the policy process. Though complete objectivity may be impossible, science at least professes a fundamental interest in reason, evidence and bias-free judgment, and offers a method for achieving these things. This marks it out from much of the political process, and accounts both for science's standing in contemporary society and its usefulness in the policy process. In effect, we have a high degree of confidence that science provides careful, factually supported, and (to some degree) value-free assessments of certain questions central to public policy.

And it is precisely this utility that the use of corrupted science threatens. If science ceases to work outside of the political and policy process, if it ceases to be a tool available to all side of an issue, if it allows itself to become enchanted and co-opted by a particular party in the policy process, if it becomes politicized and ideologically sensitive, then it ceases to be valuable in the policy process because it becomes nothing more than another special pleading, rather than the voice of reason. In short, it is the uncorrupted character of science that makes it so essential to democratic policy; corrupted, it taints the entire process. In this sense, to use corrupted science, for however allegedly worthy an end, is inevitably to invite science to corrupt itself.

The use of corrupt science to attempt to manipulate the policy process on smoking threatens not just science and the use of science in public policy, but also the standards of rationality that distinguish legitimate public policy. Adherence to the norms of rationality requires that the identification of problems, causes and solutions be based on empirical evidence of the most rigorous sort, evidence that is specific, strong, consistent, and coherent, and on rational arguments that are clear and logically compelling. Problems and solutions that cannot meet this standard of argument should not be allowed a place in the policy process. Their inclusion would mean the abandonment of commitment to reason as a foundational democratic and policy value.

The use of corrupt ETS science as a basis for public smoking and other tobacco policies is an example of this. As the Court record shows, the EPA could not demonstrate reasoned decision-making in its actions. Rather, its process and it substantive claims were based on rhetoric. Yet it proceeded to institute a *de facto* regulatory regime based on a false claim to legitimate science. Because two of the centrepieces of rationality, coherence and consistency, have been abandoned in order to make reality conform to policy, the landscape of policy has become a shifting mass of political correctness, unanchored to any scientific truth and hence unable to provide any useful guidance.

Let us consider but one example. In 1994, the *Journal of the National Cancer Institute* reported on a study of women who had had both an abortion and breast cancer (Daling et al., 1994; Rosenberg, 1994). The study noted that women who had had an abortion were 1.5 times as likely to get breast cancer as women who hadn't, a 50 percent difference in risk. Now what sort of advice should have been offered to women? Indeed, should there have been any advice? If consistency were a measure, then the precedent of the EPA's labelling of ETS as a Group A carcinogen on the basis of an RR of 1.19 would have made the answer obvious. There should certainly have been advice, and it should have been that there is a statistically significant risk of contracting breast cancer after an abortion.

However, both the press release and the editorial accompanying the article chose to downplay the presence of additional risk. The press release noted that "In epidemiologic research relative risks less than 2 are considered small and are usually difficult to interpret. Such increases may be due to chance, statistical bias, or effects of confounding factors that are sometimes not evident." The editorial said that a 50 percent increase in risk is "small in epidemiologic terms and severely challenges our ability to distinguish if it reflects cause and effect or if it simply reflects bias" (Rosenberg, 1994; Daling et al., 1994; for a further discussion of the issue see Sullum, 1996).

It is difficult to make sense of this pattern of risk determination within the bounds of coherence and consistency. The numbers and the science are strikingly similar but the risk advice is blindingly different. It would be uncharitable but probably accurate to observe that scientific consistency and coherence count for less than the importance of being politically correct about the right to an abortion. Political correctness determined the risk advice, not the evidence. This is precisely what we would expect to find when policy is disconnected from science and rationality. Risk determination and policy become *ad hoc* creatures not of science but of pre-ordained public policies.

The use of corrupt ETS science signals more, however, than simply an abandonment of reason in the public policy process. It is also something far more frightening—the attempt to institutionalize a particular irrational view of the world as the only legitimate perspective, and to replace rationality with dogma as the legitimate basis of public policy. If the use of corrupted ETS science by the EPA represented only the abandonment of reason, then their actions would be simply non-rational.

But the EPA's efforts go beyond the non-rational to the irrational, undermining the use of reason as an instrument for policy. By refusing to include evidence of scientific dissent from the officially determined truth about ETS (key bibliographies omitted any references to important studies with contrary findings), and by manipulating and misrepresenting the data, the EPA tends to appear as as an enemy of the open and self-correcting process of reason itself. At times the EPA comes perilously close to suggesting that the claim that ETS causes lung cancer is unfalsifiable in that there is apparently nothing, neither the collapse of the bio-plausibility thesis nor the statistical non-significance of the epidemiological evidence, that appears to falsify it. If true, this provides the strongest evidence of the ultimate abandonment of science for dogma, since the defining characteristic of genuine science is being subject to empirical falsification. In a very real sense, under the EPA, the truth about ETS ceases to be open to rational assessment and assumes instead the status of revealed dogma. And only those who ultimately fear, if not loath, reason are comfortable with dogma as the basis of public policy.

There is, however, a third peril that the use of corrupted ETS science poses to democratic public policy, and that is through its treatment of the question of risk. The question of risk is central to any modern discussion of harm and public policy. If much depends on science, then much depends on the science of risk assessment. And this places a special burden on those who use the notion of risk and risk assessments in policy debates to be certain that the concept is used with a fundamental integrity and not simply as a lever to frighten. In one sense, the misuse of the notion of risk is simply another instance of a basic contempt for reason in public life because it is an attempt to gain, through irrational means, something that it denied one by careful argument and compelling evidence. In order to use the notion of risk with integrity, policy discussions, statements and frameworks should, at minimum, involve:

1)   stating risk assessments in a way that does not exaggerate harm and allows individuals to make their own decisions about balancing the risks and rewards of various courses of actions;

2)   placing particular risk assessments within a general risk context in a way that allows one to compare the significance of the risk with

other risks associated with everyday living thereby changing the question from "is this activity risky?" to "does it carry a risk level that in other circumstances we would consider worrisome?";

3) conveying the full sense of both the inexactness of risk assessment (the need for bridging inferences to complete gaps in the data, for instance), and the complexity of risk assessment–even in the face of popular preference for simplicity in the face of complexity; and

4) acknowledging incorrect risk assessments and changing risk advice when warranted by new scientific evidence.

Now, given the imperatives of the Lalonde Doctrine and the general aversion of the anti-smoking movement to individual autonomy, it is obvious that these minimum standards of responsible risk discussion will be causalities of the EPA's corruption of science. Indeed, the last thing that a practitioner and purveyor of corrupted science wants to have is a careful public policy discussion about the risks of ETS along the lines set out above. For the EPA everything hinges on people thinking that the official science represents reality; and that the official scientific establishment can confidently be relied upon as a guide to the complex and confusing arena of risk.

In the end, the EPA's corrupt ETS science corrupts the entire discussion of risk in public policy by legitimizing the communication of false risk information, by failing to contextualise the risk within a framework of other accepted everyday risks, and by failing to acknowledge the complexity and consequent inexactness of its entire assessment. The failure to provide context is particularly apparent in the EPA's Group A classification of ETS on a RR of 1.19, a classification inconsistent with all of its previous work. For all its inconsistency, the study on breast cancer and abortions at least tried to provide the public some basis for understanding both the complexity of the risk assessments and the relative significance of the risks. The EPA did neither.

The fourth peril that the EPA's corrupted science presents for democratic public policy is that it undermines the value of fairness. Fairness is undermined in at least two crucial senses. First, the debate about the nature of the evidence, its complexity and its contentiousness is never fairly acknowledged. The existence of significant dissent is rarely if ever admitted and truth is made to appear as pointing unambiguously in one policy direction when, as the Court observed, this is not the case. Further, the fundamental requirements of fairness (the elicitation, examination and consideration of all views within an objective, open and non-arbitrary framework not subject to the power of authority to suppress and exclude) were flouted both in letter and in spirit by the EPA. Indeed, what emerges most clearly from the Court's judgment is a degree of scientific corruption indicative of a fundamental commitment to unfairness in the service of bogus science.

The fifth problem that the EPA's corrupt science presents for democratic public policy is its tacit creation of a semi-official, state-sanctioned scientific ideology that is used to underpin a morality that stigmatises, degrades, and excludes certain citizens from the civil community. This is, of course, over and above the criminal sanctions attaching to public smoking. This should hardly surprise for it is the ultimate and necessary purpose of the EPA's ETS science to fashion a public policy justification for marking out certain behaviour as morally unacceptable. Though the anti-smoking movement claims that its policy quarrel is with big tobacco, not with smokers, and though certain public officials portray themselves as regretful that public smoking bans will penalize smokers (it would be hard to imagine how they could not), the consequences of corrupt science are in the end felt primarily by smokers. At the very least smokers are pawns in the battle against big tobacco.

In our century, mankind has witnessed the horrible consequences of state-sanctioned science prescribing certain acceptable ways of living and thinking, and singling out certain individuals as moral reprobates. But this never seems to be mentioned in discussions about ETS and public smoking, let alone being seen as providing a warning against the dangers of giving public policy legitimacy to a scientific dogma that morally degrades and excludes.

Finally, and most significantly, the use of the EPA's corrupt ETS science in the public policy process threatens the central democratic values of autonomy, respect and diversity. The key to these values are the beliefs that individuals are equal in moral standing with the state, that they are the best judges of the shape of their own liver, that they should be encouraged to develop genuine diversity, and that they are capable of understanding and participating in the life of the community. Standing against these values is health paternalism, which starts from a dramatically different set of assumptions about the nature of people, reason, autonomy and democracy, namely:

1) that autonomy is not a foundational democratic value and that considerations of happiness and welfare must frequently take precedence over it;

2) that individuals are frequently irrational, often do not understand their interests, and do not even know how best to realise those interests; and

3) that individuals need the state's help to discover and realize their true interests, and to avoid irrational courses of action that result in unhappy consequences.

What unites these assumptions is the belief that the state is justified in restricting the rights of competent adults in order to protect them from the allegedly harmful consequences of their actions. Indeed, the most potent expression in the vocabulary of the health paternalist is "it is necessary for your own good." Based on these assumptions, health paternalism advances the following claims:

1) health is the pre-eminent value which outweighs, in most instances, all other values since a rational person would not normally place his health at risk in the interest of some other value;

2) there is but one healthy/rational way to live one's life and it does not include activities that carry with them significant risks to well-being or longevity;

3) individuals have a moral obligation to order their lives in this healthy/rational way, and

4) the state is justified, indeed has a moral obligation, to ensure that its citizens conform to this healthy/rational lifestyle, even if they are unwilling or unable to through their own efforts.

It is some version of beliefs like these that provides the ultimate motivation and justification for corrupt science. What set in motion the chain of events that led to the EPA's report was a view of the world in which people are believed to be fundamentally incapable of knowing their own interests, of understanding the world, of knowing what is best for them and fashioning their lives accordingly, and of participating in the life of their community. After all, the rationale for banning public smoking is only partly about harm to others. It also is about making it more difficult for smokers to smoke, and thus encouraging them to stop. This view of the world is utterly convinced of its own validity and utterly devoid of any interest in gaining acceptance of it through any means but manipulation and force. And it is a view of the world which has no room for either individual autonomy or respect.

If one believes these things, if one has this picture of one's fellow citizens, then it is easy to justify the use of corrupt science. Indeed, health paternalism and corrupt science are mutually re-enforcing. Health paternalism's assumptions about persons require corrupt science in order to gently guide people into the right decisions and corrupt science gains its process and substantive legitimacy from the fact that it is merely doing the good work of health paternalism—providing the evidence to prod the recalcitrant and the reluctant to what is really in their best interest. Both require bias, misrepresentation and manipulation and both are fundamentally opposed to autonomy and respect.

The very nature of corrupt science is such as to deny that individuals can, or at least can be trusted to, make important and informed decisions about themselves, and most especially about their health. The agenda of corrupted science is based at its core on the paternalistic assumptions that only a few can think and act correctly, that only a few know the truth, and that these few must therefore chart one moral, healthy and rational way to live, which the State in turn should enforce.

The EPA's went wrong at the very beginning when it decided that the interests of health paternalism and a smoke-free society should be allowed to take precedence over the central responsibility of science to tell the truth. Once having taken that fateful turning, it set itself on a course of manipulation, fabrication and misrepresentation that could not help but collide with the democratic values of autonomy, diversity and respect.

Beyond these sad and disheartening lessons for society and public policy, is there anything less gloomy that might come out of the EPA's ETS story? Is therefore, for instance, some indication that the EPA has taken notice and might change, or that the scientific establishment sees scientific misconduct as an institutional problem that should be addressed? The answer to both of these questions appears to be no.

The report of the EPA's own expert committee, convened to examine questions about the credibility of its science, reads in many places like a critique of the ETS case, even though it was published almost a year before the ETS assessment was released (USEPA, 1992e). In the report, the Agency was criticized for:

- producing science of uneven quality;

- not giving sufficient attention to validating the models, scientific assumptions and databases which it uses;

- not having a coherent science agenda and operation plan to guide scientific its efforts;

- not always conveying clearly to those outside or even inside the Agency its desire and commitment to make high-quality science a priority;

- not having a well-defined or coherently organized process to ensure that policy decisions are informed by clear understanding of relevant science;

- being perceived by many people to be willing to adjust its science to fit its policy, something which never should be done;

- not having a uniform process to ensure a minimum level of quality assurance and peer review for all the science developed in support of its decision-making;

- not always ensuring that contrasting and reputable scientific views are well-explored and well-documented from the beginning to the end of the regulatory process, and thereby undermining its role as a source of unbiased scientific information; and

- not always ensuring and it has the critical mass of externally recognized scientists needed to make its science generally credible to the wider scientific community.

It is noticeable that virtually all of the process and substantive problems identified by the Court in the ETS assessment are found here. Indeed, if the EPA had taken note of even a handful of these key problems the ETS assessment would not have proceeded as it did. This assumes, of course, that the Agency had the requisite will to change its ways. However, the fact this report was produced and released even as the corrupt ETS science process was in motion raises substantial questions about the Agency's motivation to change.

A further indication that there seems little prospect of the Agency changing comes from the fact that rather than apologizing for its process and substantive errors, acknowledging that its risk assessment was flawed and withdrawing its claim about ETS as a human carcinogen, the Agency has rejected the Court's findings and filed an appeal of Judge Osteen's decision.

What then of the wider scientific community? Might we hope for some recognition of the nature, extent and potential seriousness of corrupt science? Here again, the prospects look bleak. Despite the fact that the press often speaks about scientific misconduct, and in spite of some recent studies of the problem, (see for instance Angell's excellent analysis of the breast implant controversy, Angell, 1996) the ETS issue has generally been treated as an isolated case involving deviant individuals rather than one of institutional motivation and process subversion.

Despite these somewhat bleak prospects for hope, there are some important safeguards that might guard against corrupt science's perversion of the public policy process. One of these would be the recognition by citizens that corrupt science does exist and that it is employed in the public policy process that touches their lives. This recognition in turn would require a certain level of skepticism about all scientific pronouncements, a refusal to defer unquestioningly to authority, and the insistence that scientists provide both compelling evidence and clear and cogent argument.

Another safeguard is to be found in the law itself, or more specifically in laws like the Radon Research Act with its carefully crafted requirements for a scientific process responsible to a representative body composed of all interests and utterly open in its premises, procedures, collection of data and analysis of arguments. Such procedural and substantive requirements might still fail, but by institutionalizing transparency and fair representation as the non-negotiable framework of how science must work in the public policy process, we make scientific corruption much more difficult. And, that, perhaps is the most that we can expect.

Chapter Six

What Was Said: A Guide to the Osteen Decision

I.   The EPA's Risk Assessment Process

A)   The EPA failed to establish and consult the advisory group mandated by the Randon Research Act.

The language used in the Randon Research Act, the nature of SBA, and the composition of the IAQC which reviewed the ETS Risk Assessment, demonstrate that [the] EPA failed to comply with the procedural requirements set forth by Congress (Osteen, 1998, p. 24). No members were invited to represent or admitted to representing any constituency. Rather, [the] EPA's regulations prohibited parties with meaningful outside interests from participating (Osteen , 1998, p. 29). In the present action, [the] EPA violated a statutory procedure (Osteen, 1998, p. 33).

B)   The EPA's Risk Assessment Process was significantly flawed.

[The] EPA determined it was biologically plausible that ETS causes lung cancer. In doing so, [the] EPA recognized problems with its theory, namely the dissimilarities between MS and ETS. In other areas of the Assessment, [the] EPA relied on these dissimilarities in justifying its methodology. [The] EPA relied on these dissimilarities in justifying its methodology. [The] EPA did not explain much of the criteria and assertions upon which [the] EPA's theory relies. [The] EPA claimed selected epidemiologic studies would affirm its plausibility theory. The studies [the] EPA selected did not include a significant number of studies and data which demonstrated no association between ETS and cancer. [The] EPA did not explain its criteria for study selection, thus leaving itself open to allegations of "cherry picking" (Osteen, 1998, pp. 80-81).

C)   **Only the EPA's changed epidemiological methodology allowed it to find ETS a human carcinogen.**

Using its normal methodology and its selected studies, [the] EPA did not demonstrate a statistically significant association between ETS and lung cancer. This should have caused [the] EPA to re-evaluate the inference options used in establishing its plausibility theory. A risk assessment is supposed to entail the best judgment possible based upon the available evidence. *See Ethyl*, 541 F.2d at 24. Instead. [The] EPA changed its methodology to find a statistically significant association. [The] EPA claimed, but did not explain how, its theory justified changing the Agency's methodology. With the changed methodology and selected studies, [the] EPA established evidence of a weak statistically significant association between ETS and lung cancer (Osteen, 1998, p. 81).

D)   **The EPA reached a conclusion about ETS before beginning its research program.**

Rather than reach a conclusion after collecting information, researching, and making findings, [the] EPA categorized ETS as a "known cause of cancer" in 1989 ... in this case, [the] EPA publicly committed to a conclusion before research had begun (Osteen, 1998, p. 88-89).

E)   **The EPA's Risk Assessment Process was merely an attempt to justify its previously arrived at conclusions.**

In conducting the Assessment, [the] EPA deemed it biologically plausible that ETS was a carcinogen. [The] EPA's theory was premised on the similarities between MS, SS, and ETS. In other chapters, the Agency used MS and ETS dissimilarities to justify methodology. Recognizing problems, [the] EPA attempted to confirm the theory with epidemiological studies. After choosing a portion of the studies, [the] EPA did not find a statistically significant association. [The] EPA then claimed the bioplausibility theory, demonstrated the *a priori* hypothesis, justified a more lenient methodology. With a new methodology, [the] EPA demonstrated from the selected studies a very low relative risk for lung cancer based on ETS exposure. Based on its original theory and the weak evidence of association, [the] EPA concluded the evidence showed a causal relationship between cancer and ETS. The administrative record contains glaring deficiencies (Osteen, 1998, pp. 88-89).

F) **The EPA violated the Radon Research Act's procedural requirements at every turn.**

[The] EPA also failed the Act's procedural requirements. In the Randon Research Act, Congress granted [the] EPA limited research authority along with an obligation, to seek advice from a representative committee during such research. Congress intended industry representatives to be at the table and their voices heard during the research process. [The] EPA's authority under the act is contingent upon the Agency hearing and responding to the represented constituents' concerns. The record evidence is overwhelming that IAQC was not the representative body required under the Act. Had [the] EPA reconciled industry objections voiced from a representative body during the research process, the ETS Risk Assessment would very possibly not have been conducted in the same manner nor reached the same conclusions (Osteen, 1998, p. 91).

G) **The EPA's actions violated the clear substantive requirements of the Randon Research Act.**

In this case, [the] EPA excluded industry by violating the Act's procedural requirements; adjusted established procedure and scientific norms to validate the Agency's public conclusion, and aggressively utilized the Act's authority to disseminate findings to establish a de facto regulatory scheme intended to restrict Plaintiffs' products and to influence public opinion (Osteen, 1998, pp. 89-90).

H) **The EPA ignored evidence, suppressed evidence and findings and reached conclusions on selective evidence.**

In conducting the ETS Risk Assessment, [the] EPA disregarded information and made findings on selective information; did not disseminate significant epidemiological information; deviated from its Risk Assessment Guidelines; failed to disclose important findings and reasoning; and left significant questions without answers. [The] EPA's conduct left substantial holes in the administrative record. While so doing, [the] EPA produced limited evidence, then claimed the weight of the Agency's research evidence demonstrated ETS causes cancer (Osteen, 1998, p. 90).

I) **The EPA's obligation to determine the truth gave way to its policy agenda of demonstrating ETS a Group A carcinogen.**

Gathering all relevant information, researching, and disseminating findings were subordinate to [the] EPA's demonstrating ETS a Group A carcinogen (Osteen, 1998, p. 90).

II.   The EPA's Risk Assessment

A)   **The EPA's bioplausibility thesis—that because of the similarities between MS and ETS it is plausible that ETS is a human carcinogen—was used in a circular fashion.**

The Court is disturbed that [the] EPA and Kenneth Brown buttress the bioplausibility theory with the epidemiology studies. [The] EPA's theory must be independently plausible. [The] EPA relied upon similarities between MS and ETS to conclude that it is biologically plausible that ETS causes cancer. [The] EPA terms this theory its *"a priori* hypothesis" in justifying Chapter 5's methodology. Chapter 5's methodology allowed [the] EPA to demonstrate a statistically significant association between ETS exposure and lung cancer. See Federal Judicial Center, *Reference Manual on Scientific Evidence* 154-55, (1994) (Narrowing the confidence intervals makes it more likely that a study will be found to be statistically significant.). Chapter 5's analysis rests on the validity of the biological plausibility theory. It is circular for [the] EPA to now argue the epidemiology studies support the Agency's *a priori* theory. Without the theory, the studies would likely have done no such thing (Osteen, 1998, p. 58).

B)   **The EPA's varying assumptions about MS, SS and ETS were not based on science but on the EPA's desire to conclude that ETS is a human carcinogen.**

Since Chapter 2 found ETS and MS not sufficiently similar, Chapter 3 found them similar, and Chapter 6 found them dissimilar, [the] EPA apparently used a different risk assessment methodology for each chapter. Again, neither the Assessment nor the record explains the risk assessment components used in the different chapters, why methodologies varied between chapters, or why ETS and MS were or were not similar using each methodology (Osteen, 1998, p. 60).

The Court is faced with the ugly possibility that [the] EPA adopted a methodology for each chapter, without explanation, based on the outcome sought in that chapter. This possibility is most potent where [the] EPA rejected MS-ETS similarities to avoid a "cigarette-equivalents" analysis in determining carcinogenicity of ETS exposure. Use of cigarette-equivalent analysis may have lead to a conclusion that ETS is not a Group A carcinogen. It is striking that MS and ETS were similar only where such a conclusion promoted finding ETS a carcinogen (Osteen, 1998, p. 61).

C)   The record did not explain how similarities between SS and MS could justify classifying ETS as a human carcinogen.

The record does not support [the] EPA's arguments that [the] EPA took MS-ETS differences into account and, despite them, concluded ETS is a known human carcinogen because non-smokers are exposed to and absorb carcinogens. [The] EPA conceded that dilution, aging, and exposure characteristics fundamentally distinguish ETS from mainstream smoke, and "raise questions about the carcinogenic potential of ETS." ETS Risk Assessment at 2-7 thru 2-8, 4-29, 6-6. See also Draft Responses at 14-16 (JA 6,455-57). The record does not explain how, after raising these questions, [the] EPA could classify ETS a known human carcinogen based on similarities between SS and MS (Osteen, 1998, p. 63).

D)   The EPA's ETS Risk Assessment was rejected by the EPA's own Risk Criteria Office.

[The] EPA's Risk Criteria Office, a group of [the] EPA risk assessment experts, concluded that [the] EPA failed to reasonably explain how all relevant data on ETS, evaluated according to [the] EPA Risk Assessment Guidelines' causality criteria, can support a Group A classification (Osteen, 1998, p. 64).

E)   It was not clear that the EPA could justify its bioplausibility thesis.

In summary, Plaintiffs raise legitimate questions not addressed in the record regarding [the] EPA's bioplausibility theory. If confronted by a representative committee that voiced industry concerns, [the] EPA would likely have had to resolve these issues in the record. It is not clear whether [the] EPA could have or can do so. These issues are more than periphery (Osteen, 1998, p. 65).

F)   Without the bioplausibility thesis the just'fication for changing statistical methods collapsed.

If [the] EPA's *a priori* hypothesis fails, [the] EPA has no justification for manipulating the Agency's standard scientific methodology (Osteen, 1998, p. 65).

III.   The EPA's Choice of Epidemiological Studies

A)   The EPA provided no convincing rationale for why it choose some studies and excluded others.

The Addendum mentions the two large U.S. female non-smoker studies but does not explain why these two were excluded but the Fontham study included (Osteen, 1998, p. 67).

In its first review, IAQC stated that one of four criteria necessary to conduct a meet-analysis is a "precise definition of criteria used to include (or exclude) studies." EPA, *An SAB Report: Review of Draft Environmental Tobacco Smoke Health Effects Document*, EPA/SAB/IAQC/91/007 at 32-33 (1991) (SAB 1991 Review) (JA 9, 497-98). Regarding the studies chosen for the ETS Risk Assessment, IAQC stated:

[s]pecific criteria for including studies was not provided. The importance of this was reinforced at the Committee meeting when a re-analysis was presented on a different set of studies than those in the report. *This resulted in change in the overall risk estimate.* Decisions as to study inclusion should be made prior to analysis, based on clearly stated criteria. It is also desirable to evaluate the impact on conclusions of closely related, but excluded, studies.

Id. at 33 (first emphasis added) (JA 9, 498). In its 1992 review, neither [the] EPA or IAQC addressed again the criteria used to determine which studies were included in the meta-analysis (Osteen, 1998, p. 67).

Similarly, [the] EPA's second assertion that workplace studies were excluded because of potential cofounders is without record support (Osteen, 1998, p. 69).

[The] EPA claims it excluded the latest two U.S. spousal smoking studies because they were submitted after the close of the comment period, and [the] EPA already had a considerable database. [The] EPA claims the Fontham study was used because it published interim results, was the largest U.S. ETS study, and its methodology was superior to any other study. The record contain discussion of the Fontham study, even testimony by Dr. Fontham. However, the evidence is not relevant to Plaintiffs' assertion. There being no indication of study criteria, it is not possible to determine whether or why the Fontham study was "superior." Even if [the] EPA provided criteria, comparison would not be possible since [the] EPA provides no discussion on the two U.S. spousal studies excluded. In summary, [the] EPA's claim of having clearly established criteria is without merit (Osteen, 1998, p. 71).

B) **The EPA appears to have "cherry-picked" studies to suit its purposes.**

[The] EPA's study selection is disturbing. First there is evidence in the record supporting the association that [the] EPA "cherry-picked" its data. Without criteria for pooling studies into a meta-analysis, the Court cannot determine whether the exclusion of studies likely to disprove [the] EPA's *a priori* hypothesis was coincidence or intentional. Second, [the] EPA's excluding nearly half of the available studies directly conflicts with [the] EPA's purported purpose for analyzing the epidemiological studies and conflicts with [the] EPA's Risk Assessment Guidelines. *See* ETS Risk Assessment at 4-29 ("These data should also be examined in the interest of weighing *all the available evidence*, as recommended by [the] EPA's carcinogen risk assessment guidelines (U.S. EPA, 1986a)" ... (emphasis added)) (Osteen, 1998, p. 72).

[The] EPA claimed selected epidemiologic studies would affirm its plausibility theory. The studies [the] EPA selected did not include a significant number of studies and data which demonstrated no association between ETS and cancer. [The] EPA did not explain its criteria for study selection, thus leaving itself open to allegations of "cherry-picking" (Osteen, 1998, pp. 80-81).

C) **The EPA's exclusion of half the available data violated the EPA's own Risk Assessment guidelines and the Randon Research Act.**

Third, [the] EPA's selective use of data conflicts with the Radon Research Act. The Act states [the] EPA's program shall "gather data and information on *all aspects* of indoor air quality ... " Radon Research Act s 403(a)(i) (emphasis added). In conducting a risk assessment under the Act, [the] EPA deliberately refused to assess information on all aspects of indoor air quality (Osteen, 1998, p. 72).

D) **The EPA's information collection appears to have had little connection with its Risk Assessment.**

[The] EPA steps outside the Court's analysis when information collection becomes incidental to conducting risk management (Osteen, 1998, p. 72-73).

IV. The EPA's Epidemiologic Methodology

A)   The EPA failed to produce statistically significant results with its selected studies.

The Record and [the] EPA's explanations to the Court make it clear that using standard methodology, [the] EPA could not produce statistically significant results with its selected studies (Osteen, 1998, p. 77).

B)   The EPA could only confirm its theory that ETS was a human carcinogen by lowering the confidence interval to 90 percent.

Analysis conducted with a .05 significance level and 95 percent confidence level included relative risks of 1. Accordingly, these results did not confirm [the] EPA's controversial *a priori* hypothesis. In order to confirm its hypothesis, [the] EPA maintained its standard significance level but lowered the confidence interval to 90 percent. This allowed [the] EPA to confirm its hypothesis by finding a relative risk of 1.19 albeit a very weak association (Osteen, 1998, p. 77).

C)   The EPA provided no rationale for why it changed its epidemiologic methodology.

The Court's conclusions regarding [the] EPA's motive for reducing the confidence level are based upon [the] EPA's litigation explanations and circumstantial evidence from the record. [The] EPA does not provide explanation in the ETS Risk Assessment or administrative record. When an agency changes its methodology mid-stream, as [the] EPA did here, it has an obligation to explain why (Osteen, 1998, p. 78).

D)   The EPA attempted to suppress significant findings in order to confirm its bioplausibility theory.

Finally, when an agency conducts activities under an act authorizing information collection and dissemination of findings, the agency has a duty to disseminate the findings made. [The] EPA did not disclose in the record or in the Assessment: its inability to demonstrate a statistically significant relationship under normal methodology; the reasoning behind adopting a one-tailed test, or that only after adjusting the Agency's methodology could a weak relative risk be demonstrated. Instead of disclosing information, the Agency withheld insignificant portions of its findings and reasoning in striving to confirm its *a priori* hypothesis (Osteen, 1998, p. 78-79).

E) **The EPA's normal methodology, even using only selected studies, could not produce a statistically significant association between ETS's and lung cancer.**

[The] EPA's conduct raises several concerns besides whether a relative risk of 1.19 is credible evidence supporting a Group A classification. First, with such a weak showing, if even a fraction of Plaintiffs' allegations regarding study selection or methodology is true, [the] EPA cannot show a statistically significant association between ETS and lung cancer (Osteen, 1998, pp. 77-78).

Using its normal methodology and its selected studies, [the] EPA did not demonstrate a statistically significant association between ETS and lung cancer. This should have caused [the] EPA to re-evaluate the inference options used in establishing its plausibility theory. A risk assessment is supposed to entail the best judgment possible based upon the available evidence. *See Ethyl*, 541 F.2d at 24. Instead [the] EPA changed its methodology to find a statistically significant association. [The] EPA claimed, but did not explain how, its theory justified changing the Agency's methodology. With the changed methodology and selected studies, [the] EPA established evidence of a weak statistically significant association between ETS and lung cancer (Osteen, 1998, p. 81).

Appendix:

Judge Osteen's Decision

IN THE UNITED STATES DISTRICT COURT
FOR THE MIDDLE DISTRICT OF NORTH CAROLINA
WINSTON-SALEM DIVISION

FLUE-CURED TOBACCO COOPERATIVE   )
STABILIZATION CORPORATION,   )
THE COUNCIL FOR BURLEY TOBACCO,   )
INC.,   )
UNIVERSAL LEAF TOBACCO COMPANY,   )
INCORPORATED,   )
PHILIP MORRIS INCORPORATED,   )
R.J. REYNOLDS TOBACCO COMPANY,   )
and   )
GALLINS VENDING COMPANY,   )
)
          Plaintiffs,   )
)
     v.   )   6:93CV00370
)
UNITED STATES ENVIRONMENTAL   )
PROTECTION AGENCY, and   )
CAROL BROWNER, Administrator,   )
Environmental Protection   )
Agency,   )
)
          Defendants.   )

ORDER AND JUDGMENT

OSTEEN, District Judge

For the reasons set forth in the memorandum opinion entered
contemporaneously herewith,

IT IS ORDERED AND ADJUDGED that Plaintiffs' Motion for
Partial Summary Judgment is granted [117].

IT IS FURTHER ORDERED AND ADJUDGED that Defendants' Cross Motion for Summary Judgment is denied [126]. The court vacates Chapters 1-6 of and the Appendices to EPA's <u>Respiratory Health Effects of Passive Smoking: Lung Cancer and Other Disorders</u>, EPA/600/6-90/006F (December 1992). To ripen its judgment for purposes of appellate review, pursuant to Federal Rule of Civil Procedure 54(b), the court finds there is no just reason for delaying entry of judgment.

IT IS FURTHER ORDERED AND ADJUDGED that Plaintiffs' Motion for Leave to File Supplement Pleading under Rule 15(d) is granted [120].

This the 17th day July 1998.

_____
United States District Judge

IN THE UNITED STATES DISTRICT COURT
FOR THE MIDDLE DISTRICT OF NORTH CAROLINA
WINSTON-SALEM DIVISION

FLUE-CURED TOBACCO COOPERATIVE)
STABILIZATION CORPORATION,)
THE COUNCIL FOR BURLEY TOBACCO,)
INC.,)
UNIVERSAL LEAF TOBACCO COMPANY,)
INCORPORATED,)
PHILIP MORRIS INCORPORATED,)
R.J. REYNOLDS TOBACCO COMPANY,)
and)
GALLINS VENDING COMPANY,)
)
      Plaintiffs,)
)
   v.)   6:93CV00370
)
UNITED STATES ENVIRONMENTAL)
PROTECTION AGENCY, and)
CAROL BROWNER, Administrator,)
Environmental Protection)
Agency,)
)
      Defendants.)

FILED
JUL 17 1998
IN THIS OFFICE
Clerk, U.S. District Court
Greensboro, N.C.
BY ....

MEMORANDUM OPINION

OSTEEN, District Judge

    This case is before the court on the parties' cross motions
for partial summary judgment on Counts I-III of the Complaint.
These counts raise Administrative Procedure Act (APA) challenges
to EPA's report, <u>Respiratory Health Effects of Passive Smoking:</u>
<u>Lung Cancer and Other Disorders</u>, EPA/600/6-90/006F, December 1992

(ETS Risk Assessment). EPA claims its authority to conduct the
ETS Risk Assessment derives from the Radon Gas and Indoor Air
Quality Research Act of 1986, Pub. L. No. 99-499, 100 Stat.
1758-60 (1986) (Radon Research Act) (codified at 42 U.S.C. § 7401
note (1994)). In the ETS Risk Assessment, EPA evaluated the
respiratory health effects of breathing secondhand smoke
(environmental tobacco smoke or ETS) and classified ETS as a
Group A carcinogen, a designation meaning there is sufficient
evidence to conclude ETS causes cancer in humans. Disputing the
Assessment, Plaintiffs argue: EPA exceeded its authority under
and violated the restrictions within the Radon Research Act; EPA
did not comply with the Radon Research Act's procedural
requirements; EPA violated administrative law procedure by making
a conclusion regarding ETS before it concluded its risk
assessment, and EPA's ETS Risk Assessment was not the result of
reasoned decision making.[1] EPA denies the same and argues the
administrative record (record) demonstrates reasoned decision
making. Plaintiffs have also filed a motion to supplement the

_____

[1] Plaintiffs also allege that EPA's issuance of the ETS
Risk Assessment violated Plaintiffs' due process rights. The
court has stayed consideration of the due process claims pending
resolution of the APA claims. See Flue-Cured Tobacco Cooperative
Stabilization Corp. v. EPA, 857 F. Supp. 1137 (M.D.N.C. 1994).

pleadings. For the reasons stated herein, the court will enter
an order granting Plaintiffs' motions.

I.   **THE RADON RESEARCH ACT**

The Radon Research Act was enacted by Congress as Title IV
of the Superfund Amendments and Reauthorization Act of 1986
(SARA) and codified with the Clean Air Act at 42 U.S.C. § 7401
note. The Act was based on Congress' finding: "exposure to
naturally occurring radon and indoor air pollutants poses public
health risk[s]," id. § 402(2); "Federal radon and indoor air
pollutant research programs are fragmented and underfunded," id.
§ 402(3); and an "information base concerning exposure to radon
and indoor air pollutants should be developed . . . ." Id.
§ 402(4). The act provides

> (a) **Design of Program.** - [The EPA] shall establish
> a research program with respect to radon gas and
> indoor air quality. Such program shall be
> designed to -
>
> > (1) gather data and information on all
> > aspects of indoor air quality in order
> > to contribute to the understanding of
> > health problems associated with the
> > existence of air pollutants in the
> > indoor environment;
> >
> > (2) coordinate Federal, State, local,
> > and private research and development

3

efforts relating to the improvement of
indoor air quality; and

(3) assess appropriate Federal
Government actions to mitigate the
environmental and health risks
associated with indoor air quality
problems.

(b) **Program requirements.** - The research program
required under this section shall include -

(1) research and development concerning
the identification, characterization,
and monitoring of the sources and levels
of indoor air pollution . . . .

. . . .

(2) research relating to the effects of
indoor air pollution and radon on human
health;

. . . .

(6) the dissemination of information to
assure the public availability of the
findings of the activities under this
section.

Id. § 403(a) & (b). Congress also required a narrow

construction of the authority delegated under the Radon Research

Act. Nothing in the act "shall be construed to authorize the

[EPA] to carry out any regulatory program or any activity other

than research, development, and related reporting, information

dissemination, and coordination activities specified in [the

Radon Research Act]." Id. § 404.

4

The Act _requires_ EPA to establish two advisory groups to
assist EPA in carrying out its statutory obligations under the
Radon Research Act. One of the advisory groups is to be a
committee comprised of representatives of federal agencies
concerned with various aspects of indoor air quality, and the
other group is to be "an advisory group comprised of individuals
representing the States, the scientific community, industry, and
public interest organizations . . . ." _Id._ § 403(c). The Act
requires EPA to submit its research plan to the EPA Science
Advisory Board which, in turn, would submit comments to Congress.
_Id._ § 403(d).

II. STANDARD OF REVIEW[2]

Administrative agencies have no power to act beyond
authority conferred by Congress. _See, e.g., Louisiana Public
Serv. Comm'n v. FCC_, 476 U.S. 355, 374, 206 S. Ct. 1890, 1901, 90
L. Ed. 2d 369 (1986). Title 5 U.S.C. § 706(2)(C) requires the

---

[2] As this case involves review of administrative agency
action, the court will not conduct _de novo_ review but must review
the record before EPA at the time EPA made its decision. For a
discussion on the scope of review, see _Flue-Cured Tobacco
Cooperative Stabilization Corp. v. EPA_, No. 6:93CV00370 at 16-20
(M.D.N.C. May 23, 1995) (Memorandum Opinion discussing summary
judgment on scope of review).

court to "hold unlawful and set aside agency action . . . found to be . . . in excess of statutory jurisdiction, authority, or limitations, or short of statutory right." The initial inquiry for judicial review of agency action is "whether Congress has directly spoken to the precise question at issue. If the intent of Congress is clear, that is the end of the matter; for the court, as well as the agency, must give effect to the unambiguously expressed intent of Congress." Chevron, U.S.A., Inc. v. Natural Resources Defense Council, Inc., 467 U.S. 837, 842-43, 104 S. Ct. 2778, 2781, 81 L. Ed. 2d 694 (1984). "The task of resolving the dispute over the meaning of [the statute] begins where all such inquiries must begin: with the language of the statute itself." United States v. Ron Pair Enter., Inc., 489 U.S. 235, 241, 109 S. Ct. 1026, 1030, 103 L. Ed. 2d 290 (1989) (citations omitted). "The judiciary . . . is the final authority on issues of statutory construction and will reject administrative interpretations which are contrary to the clear congressional intent." Adams v. Dole, 927 F.2d 771, 774 (4th Cir. 1991).

"[I]f the statute is silent or ambiguous with respect to the specific issue, the question for the court is whether the agency's answer is based on a permissible construction of the

6

statute." Chevron, 467 U.S. at 843, 104 S. Ct. at 2782. Courts

do not always abide by this Chevron deference. Although the

circuits appear divided, the majority of post-Chevron cases hold

no deference is accorded to an agency's view of a statute where

the statute does not confer rule making authority on the agency.

Compare Merck & Co. v. Kessler, 80 F.3d 1543, 1550 (Fed. Cir.

1996) (Chevron does not apply to interpretive rules); Atchison,

Topeka & Santa Fe Ry. v. Pena, 44 F.3d 437, 441-42 (7th Cir.

1994) (en banc) (same), aff'd on other grounds sub nom.

Brotherhood of Locomotive Eng'rs v. Atchison, Topeka & Santa Fe

Ry., 116 S. Ct. 595 (1996) with Trans Union Corp. v. FTC, 81 F.3d

228, 230-31 (D.C. Cir. 1996) (applying Chevron to interpretive

rule); Elizabeth Blackwell Health Ctr. for Women v. Knoll, 61

F.3d 170, 182 (3d Cir. 1995) (same), cert. denied, 116 S. Ct. 816

(1996). See Ronald M. Levin, Scope of Review Legislation: The

Lessons of 1995, 31 Wake Forest L. Rev. 647, 662-64 (1996).

Another factor in determining an agency's discretion in statutory

interpretation is the specificity of interpretation. Courts

determine the general meaning of legislation, whereas agencies

are often better equipped to determine interstitial meanings.

John H. Reese, Administrative Law Principles and Practice 709-713

(1995).

III. EPA's AUTHORITY UNDER THE RADON RESEARCH ACT

The parties assert the plain language of the statute determines whether EPA had authority to assess the risks of and classify ETS. The court agrees. However, the parties, reading the plain language, come to opposite conclusions. Plaintiffs argue EPA exceeded its statutory grant of authority under the Radon Research Act by conducting a risk assessment, making a carcinogen classification, and by engaging in de facto regulation. Plaintiffs also argue the Toxic Substance Control Act prohibited EPA's risk assessment of ETS.

A. The Radon Research Act Authorizes EPA's Risk Assessment and Classification of Environmental Tobacco Smoke.

Plaintiffs concede EPA was authorized to conduct research on ETS and indoor air quality but argue EPA's ETS carcinogen risk assessment and carcinogen classification are regulatory activities, not research activities. EPA's Guidelines for Carcinogen Risk Assessment, 51 Fed. Reg. 33,992, 33,993 (1986) (Risk Assessment Guidelines) state: "[r]egulatory decision making involves two components: risk assessment and risk management." See also, 60 Fed. Reg. 52,032, 52,034 (1995) (Risk assessment is a component of the regulatory process.).

8

Plaintiffs also rely on the National Resource Council's (NRC) Redbook which recognizes risk assessment as a distinct element of the regulatory process. See NRC, Risk Assessment in the Federal Government: Managing the Process 3 (1983) (NRC Redbook). Plaintiffs argue that since risk assessment is a component of regulatory activity, risk assessment is not authorized research but rather proscribed regulatory activity.

EPA's Risk Assessment Guidelines state risk assessment incorporates judgmental positions and the Agency's regulatory mission. Risk Assessment Guidelines at 33,994. Plaintiffs also offer evidence that EPA has promulgated regulations for every other substance for which it has conducted a risk assessment and classified the substance as a Group A carcinogen.[3] Thus, Plaintiffs conclude that EPA's guidelines and actions demonstrate risk assessment is a regulatory, not research, tool.

In arguing EPA recognizes this distinction between risk assessment and research, Plaintiffs offer evidence that EPA is assessing the risks of several other indoor air pollutants, none of which are being conducted under the authority of the Radon

---

[3] See Assessing the Effects of Environmental Tobacco Smoke: Hearing on S. 262 and S. 1680 Before the Subcomm. on Clean Air and Nuclear Reg. of the Sen. Comm. on Env't and Public Works, 103d Cong. 177, 204-05 (1994) (Browner Hearing Responses).

Research Act. Included is evidence that EPA did not conduct its
risk assessment of radon under the authority of the Radon
Research Act.[4] Instead, EPA relied on the Toxic Substance
Control Act (TSCA), 15 U.S.C. §§ 2601 et seq., which authorizes
EPA to describe "action levels indicating the health risk
associated with different levels of radon exposure." TSCA
§ 2663(b)(1).[5] Plaintiffs argue EPA's reliance on TSCA indicates
EPA realizes the Radon Research Act does not authorize risk
assessments or carcinogenic classifications.

EPA replies that the Radon Research Act provides a broad
mandate to conduct activities short of actual regulation. Upon a
sparse legislative record and subsequent congressional funding,
EPA urges that Congress intended the act to include ETS.

The court is not persuaded by Plaintiffs' arguments or EPA's
reliance on what certain members of Congress intended. The plain
language of the statute is sufficient to resolve this dispute.
In the Radon Research Act, Congress directed EPA to gather
information on all aspects of indoor air quality, research indoor

_____

[4] See Browner Hearing Responses at 190-92.

[5] Plaintiffs also provide evidence that EPA did not include
the ETS project when providing Congress with a listing of Agency
research activity.

pollutants' effects on health, characterize sources of pollution, and disseminate the findings. Determining whether Congress authorized risk assessments requires defining risk assessment. "Risk assessment is the use of the factual base to define the health effects of exposure of individuals or populations to hazardous materials and situations." NRC Redbook, at 3. "[NRC] use[s] risk assessment to mean the characterization of the potential adverse health effects of human exposures to environmental hazards." Id. at 18. "The qualitative assessment or hazard identification part of risk assessment contains a review of the relevant biological and chemical information bearing on whether or not an agent may pose a carcinogenic hazard." Risk Assessment Guidelines at 33,994.

> Risk assessments include several elements: description of the potential adverse health effects based on an evaluation of results of epidemiologic, clinical, toxicologic, and environmental research; extrapolation from those results to predict the type and estimate the extent of health effects in humans under given conditions of exposure; judgments as to the number and characteristics of persons exposed at various intensities and durations; and summary judgments on the existence and overall magnitude of the public-health problem. Risk assessment also includes characterization of the uncertainties inherent in the process of inferring risk.

NRC Redbook, at 18.

11

In researching effects on health, EPA must assess whether pollutants are hazardous to health. Researching whether pollutants are hazardous to health necessarily entails assessing the risk such pollutants pose to health. Thus, researching health effects is indistinguishable from assessing risk to health. Congress' directives to research the effects of indoor air pollution on human health and disseminate the findings encompass risk assessment as defined by NRC and explained by EPA's Risk Assessment Guidelines.

The NRC explains "description of the potential adverse health effects" is a component of risk assessment. Id. The Radon Research Act requires researching pollutants' effects on health and disseminating the findings. The mandate of the Act requires more of EPA than merely describing effects. Congress intended EPA to disseminate findings, or conclusions, based upon the information researched and gathered. Utilizing descriptions of health effects to make findings is risk assessment.

The Radon Research Act contains two independent directives which authorize EPA to classify indoor pollutants as carcinogenic. First, Congress required EPA to characterize sources of indoor air pollution. Radon Research Act § 403(b)(1). Since they emit gasses and particulates, burning cigarettes are a

12

source of indoor air pollutants. By determining whether these emissions cause cancer in people exposed to burning cigarettes, EPA is characterizing a source of indoor air pollution. Second, Congress required EPA to determine indoor pollutants' effects on health. Id. § 403(b)(2). In determining whether health is affected by a pollutant, the researcher must identify whether a causal relationship exists between the pollutant and deteriorating health. Put simply, the researcher must determine how, if at all, a pollutant affects health. Once a researcher has identified how a pollutant harms human health, the risk is most often identified.[6] This is especially true regarding carcinogens. The Radon Research Act's general language authorizing EPA to characterize sources of pollutants, research effects on health, and disseminate the findings encompasses classifying pollutants based on their effects.

---

[6] For example, if research determines a pollutant harms human health by causing malignant tumors, it is ipso facto a carcinogen. See Ted A. Loomis & A. Wallace Hayes, Essentials of Toxicology 232-36 (4th ed. 1996) (tests for carcinogenicity). If research determines the pollutant causes blockage of neurotransmissions, it is ipso facto a neurotoxin. See David R. Franz, et al., Clinical Recognition and Management of Patients Exposed to Biological Warfare Agents, 278 JAMA 399 (1997) (discussing botulinum toxins).

13

The court is not persuaded by Plaintiffs' evidence showing
risk assessment incorporates judgmental positions and an agency's
regulatory mission. Researching how a pollutant affects health
entails conducting risk assessment. Judgment and inference do
not automatically remove risk assessment from what constitutes
researching health effects. To the contrary, judgment and
inference inhere in the "use of [a] factual base to define the
health effects of exposure of individuals or populations to
hazardous materials and situations." NRC Redbook, at 3, 18, 28.
"Risk assessment . . . includes characterization of the
uncertainties inherent in the process of inferring risk." Id. at
18.

> The uncertainties inherent in risk assessment can
> be grouped in two general categories: missing or
> ambiguous information on a particular substance
> and gaps in current scientific theory. When
> scientific uncertainty is encountered in the risk
> assessment process, inferential bridges are needed
> to allow the process to continue. . . . The
> judgments made by the scientist/risk assessor for
> each component of risk assessment often entail a
> choice among several scientifically plausible
> options; the Committee has designated these
> inference options.

Id. at 28. In conducting a scientific inquiry into whether a
pollutant affects human health, a researcher will have to choose
inference options. In fulfilling its obligation under the Radon

Research Act, EPA must adopt inference options in conducting research, characterizing, and making findings. Inference options that are scientifically plausible and fundamentally fair are part of risk assessment. EPA may conduct risk assessments under the Radon Research Act so long as the assessments do not impede the Act's general requirements of gathering all relevant information, researching, and disseminating the findings.

The court disagrees with Plaintiffs' argument that risk assessment constitutes a regulatory activity and is thus prohibited under the Radon Research Act. Both the NRC's Redbook and EPA's Risk Assessment Guidelines identify regulatory activity as being comprised of two elements: risk assessment and risk management. Prohibition of certain conduct does not include prohibition of lesser included activities.[7] Prohibiting conduct entails a prohibition against conducting the lesser included activities in concert to arrive at the proscribed result. Risk assessment is a component of regulation. Congress' prohibition of regulation is not a prohibition against the components comprising regulation. In the Radon Research Act, Congress intended EPA to research, collect, and disseminate information

---

[7] Standing upright is a component of running. A prohibition on running is not also a prohibition on standing.

and findings on indoor air pollutants' effect on health without

engaging in regulating. Risk assessments are incidental to

researching effects on health, characterizing sources of

pollutants, and making findings. So long as collecting and

researching information and disseminating the resulting

information are EPA's lodestar, Congress' prohibiting regulation

under the Radon Research Act does not preclude risk assessment.

The court will review the ETS Risk Assessment to determine

whether EPA conducted its research activities in accordance with

the Act.

Finally, Plaintiffs' evidence of EPA's reliance on other

statutes for assessing risks of other indoor air pollutants is

not persuasive. In these statutes, Congress granted EPA

regulatory power over certain pollutants. EPA has since

promulgated regulations pursuant to these statutes. It is

unremarkable that when asked its authority to conduct elements of

its regulatory process from which regulation occurred, EPA cited

the statutes granting full regulatory power.[8]

---

[8] Even if it were persuasive evidence that EPA interpreted
the Radon Research Act to exclude risk assessment, the court
makes its determination based upon the language Congress used,
not agency interpretation.

16

B.   EPA's Environmental Tobacco Smoke Activities Do Not
     Constitute a Prohibited Regulatory Program Under the
     Radon Research Act.

Plaintiffs have shown that EPA aggressively

disseminated information, coordinated activities with government

agencies and non-governmental organizations, and promoted ETS

regulation and prohibition.[9] Plaintiffs argue EPA's conduct

constitutes de facto regulatory activity in violation of the

Radon Research Act.

---

[9] See, e.g., Summary of EPA Draft Conclusions and SAB
Review, Steven Bayard, EPA ETS Project Manager, ORD Q.9 at 1
(April 4, 1991) (Joint Appendix (JA) 6,700) ("EPA has no
regulatory authority on ETS, but is coordinating with OSHA which
does have regulatory authority in the workplace."); EPA
Memorandum from William G. Rosenberg, Assistant Administrator for
Air and Radiation, to Erich W. Bretthauer, Assistant
Administrator for Research and Development at 1 (Oct. 7, 1991)
(JA 6,696-97) (urging expedition of ETS study; local, state and
federal agency projects awaiting its issuance); EPA Memorandum
from William G. Rosenberg, Assistant Administrator for Air and
Radiation, to Donald G. Barnes, Director, Science Advisory Board
(June 28, 1991), and attached ETS Technical Compendium, Draft
(May 1991) at 2 (JA 6,755-56, 6,758) (intended to help state
legislators ban smoking in workplaces, restaurants, and public
places).

EPA's activities did not amount to formal regulation,[10] for it issued no regulations and made no attempt to directly manage ETS risks. EPA's activities constituted de facto regulatory activity but were achieved through means authorized by Congress. Congress prohibited any regulatory program or activity "other than research, development, and related reporting, information dissemination, and coordination activities . . . ." Radon Research Act § 404 (emphasis added). EPA may be using its authority under the Act more aggressively and effectively than Congress had foreseen, however, such activities are within the law as written. Removal of EPA's authority to engage in de facto regulatory activity under the Radon Research Act requires an act of Congress, not the court's judgment.

C.   **The Toxic Substance Control Act's Prohibition With Respect to Tobacco Does Not Apply to the Radon Research Act.**

In the Toxic Substance Control Act (TSCA), Congress authorized EPA to regulate chemical substances presenting an

---

[10]   Plaintiffs also seek leave to supplement the pleadings, claiming EPA is promulgating indoor air regulations by funding and controlling a private entity that drafts indoor air ventilation standards that are adopted in state and local building codes. The court does not consider these allegations in ruling on the parties' summary judgment motions.

unreasonable risk of injury to health or the environment. 15
U.S.C. § 2605. TSCA does not authorize EPA to regulate tobacco
products. Id. § 2602(2)(B)(iii). Some in Congress have
attempted to repeal the tobacco exemption for the purpose of
providing EPA with authority to regulate tobacco smoke under
TSCA. See 136 Cong. Rec. E2223, E2224 (daily ed. June 28, 1990)
(statement of Rep. Luken). More recently, a bill was introduced
to amend TSCA "to protect the public from health hazards caused
by exposure to [ETS]." S. 1680, 103d Cong., 1st Sess., 139 Cong.
Rec. S16222 (daily ed. Nov. 18, 1993). Both bills were
introduced after the enactment of the Radon Research Act, and
neither passed. Plaintiffs argue the specific language in TSCA,
regarding tobacco, takes precedence over the general conflicting
language of the Radon Research Act.

The court does not find the conflict Plaintiffs' argument
presumes. In the TSCA, Congress directed EPA to prohibit, limit,
and regulate the manufacture, processing, or distribution of
hazardous chemical substances. Congress exempted tobacco from
TSCA's regulatory reach. The Radon Research Act contains no
regulatory authority. Compare TSCA § 2605 (EPA's requirements in
regulating manufacturing, processing, and distribution of
hazardous chemical substances), with Radon Research Act § 404 (no

19

regulatory authority except research, development, dissemination, and coordination regarding indoor air pollutants).

To the extent the Radon Research Act authorizes de facto regulatory activity, Congress simply excluded tobacco from the definition of chemical substance as used in the TSCA chapter. See TSCA § 2602 (definitions "As used in this chapter"). Congress' defining "chemical substance" under the TSCA to exclude tobacco does not mean Congress conclusively removed tobacco from EPA's jurisdiction. It means Congress removed tobacco from the authority granted to EPA under TSCA. Congress did not so limit the definition of "indoor air pollutant" under the Radon Research Act. See generally Coyne Beahm, Inc. v. FDA, 966 F. Supp. 1374, 1379-80 (M.D.N.C. 1997) (declining to infer preemption of FDA authority to regulate tobacco products from other tobacco-specific legislation or Congress' failure to act). There being no conflict between the statutes and finding Congress' TSCA restriction by definition inapplicable to the Radon Research Act, Plaintiffs' argument fails.

IV. **EPA's PROCEDURAL REQUIREMENTS UNDER THE RADON RESEARCH ACT**

Plaintiffs argue EPA failed to establish and consult the advisory group mandated by the Radon Research Act, therefore,

EPA's conduct under the Act was unlawful and must be vacated.
EPA responds by arguing it satisfied its procedural requirements
by consulting the EPA Science Advisory Board (SAB). EPA states
it formed an advisory group within SAB which included
representatives of all the statutorily identified constituencies.
EPA further argues that even if it did not satisfy the Radon
Research Act's procedural requirements: (1) the Act speaks in
general terms and committee formation was not a prerequisite to
research activity under the Act, and (2) Plaintiffs were not
prejudiced because EPA utilized public participation and peer
review procedures in developing the ETS Risk Assessment. In
reply, Plaintiffs analyze SAB and the members of the board which
reviewed the ETS Risk Assessment.

A.   Background

"[T]he SAB is an independent group of non-Federal
government scientists and engineers who are mandated through the
Environmental Research, Development and Demonstration Act of 1978
to provide advice to the EPA Administrator on technical aspects
of issues confronting the Agency." EPA Memorandum from William
K. Reilly, Administrator, to Congressman Thomas J. Bliley, Jr.,
U.S. House of Representatives 1 (Oct. 11, 1990) (Reilly Mem.) (JA

21

9,310). See also, 42 U.S.C. § 4365 (statute authorizing SAB).

"The objective of the Board is to provide independent advice . .

. . The Board will review scientific issues, provide independent

scientific and technical advice on EPA's major programs and

perform special assignments . . . ." SAB Charter ¶ 3, reprinted

in, EPA, U.S. Environmental Protection Agency Advisory Committees

137 (July 1994) (JA 3,445). "[T]he Board augments its standing

committee membership with the inclusion of subject-matter experts

('consultants') to provide special insights on particular issues.

In identifying appropriate consultants, the [SAB] . . . solicits

names of candidates from a variety of public and private sources,

which generally include the Agency and the affected parties."

Reilly Mem. at 2 (JA 9,311). SAB then attempts to select experts

from "either side of the middle of the spectrum of views in the

technical community, with few, if any, coming from either end of

the spectrum." Id. at 1 (JA 9,310).

In 1986, Congress passed the Radon Research Act which

required that EPA "establish . . . an advisory group comprised of

individuals representing the States, the scientific community,

industry, and public interest organizations to assist [EPA] in

carrying out the research program for . . . indoor air quality."

Radon Research Act § 403(c). The Act also required EPA to submit

22

its research plan to SAB. *Id.* § 403(d). In response, "the SAB
established the Indoor Air Quality/Total Human Exposure Committee
(IAQC) as the forum in which the SAB would consider indoor air
issues." Reilly Mem. at 1 (JA 9,310).

An EPA Ethics Advisory sent to IAQC draws the distinction
between "representatives" on advisory committees and "Special
Government Employees." EPA Memorandum from Robert Flaak,
Assistant Staff Director, SAB, to IAQC at Enclosure G[11] (June 17,
1992) (JA 10,938-40) (Flaak Mem.). Representatives are those who
"appear in a representative capacity to speak for firms or an
industry . . . or for any other recognizable group . . . ,"
whereas "Special Government Employees" do not. *Id.* (JA 10,940).
Another attachment, captioned "Procedures for Public Disclosures
at SAB Meetings," states the IAQC panel members were serving as
Special Government Employees, not as representatives: "SAB
members and consultants (M/Cs) carry our [sic] their duties as
Special Government Employees (SGE's) and are subject to the COI
[conflict of interest] regulations." *Id.* at Enclosure F (JA

---

[11] Enclosure G: EPA Memorandum from Gerald Yamada,
Principal Deputy General Counsel, Designated Agency Ethics
Official, to Deputy Ethics Officials (April 24, 1992).

10,936). See 18 U.S.C. §§ 202-09 (restrictions on special

government employees).

B. Neither the Science Advisory Board Or Its Subcommittee Is the Representative Advisory Group Congress Mandated In the Radon Research Act.

The language used in the Radon Research Act, the nature

of SAB, and the composition of the IAQC which reviewed the ETS

Risk Assessment, demonstrate that EPA failed to comply with the

procedural requirements set forth by Congress. In § 403(c) of

the Radon Research Act, Congress clearly requires EPA to

establish a representative advisory group to assist EPA in

carrying out research programs conducted under the Act. The

group is to be comprised of representatives from the states,

scientific community, industry, and public interest

organizations. In the following paragraph, § 403(d), Congress

requires that EPA submit its research plan "to the EPA Science

Advisory Board . . .," which would then submit its comments to

Congress. "Where Congress includes particular language in one

section of a statute but omits it in another section of the same

Act, it is generally presumed that Congress acts intentionally

and purposely in the disparate inclusion or exclusion." Brown v.

24

Gardner, 513 U.S. 115, 120, 115 S. Ct. 552, 556, 130 L. Ed. 2d 462 (1994)(citation omitted). The presumption is strengthened where, as here, the disparate language is used within the same section. Had Congress meant SAB when requiring a representative advisory group, Congress would have specified SAB as it did in the subsequent paragraph. Further, § 403(c) calls upon EPA to establish the advisory group. In 1977, Congress mandated creation of SAB, and EPA complied. Congress' use of "establish" suggests that EPA should create a group. Congress would not likely direct EPA to establish what already exists. A closer examination of SAB verifies the court's statutory construction.

Congress directed EPA to establish and consult a representative group to assist EPA in conducting research under the Radon Research Act. To "represent" or be a "representative," one must possess the ability to "speak or act with authority on behalf of," or "act as [a] substitute or agent" for the person or interest represented.[12] Black's Law Dictionary 1301 (6th ed. 1990). In contrast, EPA designed SAB to provide independent

---

[12] The legislative history supports this common sense interpretation of "represent." Senator Lautenberg, one of the sponsors of the bill that became the Radon Research Act, said the Advisory Committee was to be "a blue ribbon advisory committee, composed of members" of the specified constituencies. 131 Cong. Rec. S11684 (daily ed. Sept. 18, 1985) (JA 657).

advice. EPA designated SAB employees as special government employees (SGE's), meaning the employees are temporarily appointed, "as contrasted with members who are designated as 'representatives' . . . ." Flaak Mem. at Enclosure G (JA 10,938). SGE's may not participate in matters that affect their employers' financial interests.[13] Id. (JA 10,939). Congress' requiring a collegium of representatives is incompatible with SAB's independent and aspiringly neutral composition. Both the role Congress assigned to each group and the composition of the group that provided advice on the ETS Risk Assessment provides further evidence of this incompatibility.

Congress set forth in § 403(d) a role for the SAB that tracks the SAB's traditional mission: providing independent scientific review and comment on EPA's plan for implementing the research program. In contrast, § 403(c) charged the advisory group with representing specified constituencies and providing assistance to EPA in carrying out the research program. Those are two different roles for two different groups.

---

[13] EPA may waive conflicts where the interest affected is insubstantial or the need for the SGE's service outweighs the conflict.

The IAQC group that provided advice to EPA on the ETS Risk Assessment was not the representative body required by § 403(c). See ETS Risk Assessment at xviii-xx. In the ETS Risk Assessment, EPA lists nine members of IAQC who participated in the reviews of two review drafts. Seven of the members are listed as university professors or members of schools, one was listed as a scientist in a national laboratory, and one was a state employee. Of the nine consultants involved, seven were employed by universities, and two by special interest groups. EPA claims that one of the listed members, Dr. Woods, represented industry. However, this is not possible since Dr. Woods left industry for employment with a university almost a year before the first draft of the ETS Risk Assessment was made available for review by IAQC. See JA 7,063-73 (Dr. Wood's curriculum vita). EPA further asserts that two other individuals represented industry. The ETS Risk Assessment IAQC listing does not contain the names of these individuals. The individuals are not listed in the IAQC ETS reviews' transcripts,[14] nor does EPA assert or direct the court's

---

[14] See U.S. EPA SAB IAQC ETS Review, I.SAB.16.1 & .2 (December 4 & 5, 1990) (transcript volumes I & II) (1990 IAQC Transcript) (JA 8,793-9,213); U.S. EPA SAB IAQC ETS Review Panel, II.SAB.8.1 & .2 (July 21 & 22, 1992) (transcript volumes I & II) (1992 IAQC Transcript) (JA 11,641-12,105).

attention to evidence that these individuals provided any participation in the ETS Risk Assessment.

EPA points out that some panelists were associated with organizations that had received some industry funding pursuant to contract. That does not convert those individuals into industry representatives under § 403(c). EPA also urges that one of the panelists was selected as a consultant on the recommendation of the tobacco industry. Appropriately, EPA does not attempt to argue that one becomes a member or representative of industry upon a recommendation by industry.

EPA confirmed IAQC's independence from outside interests. When he was preparing the panel for the second public meeting on the draft ETS Risk Assessment, the SAB assistant director included in his transmittal letter a reminder to panel members of their conflict of interest and disclosure obligations:

> An area of potential sensitivity in our public meetings is the nature of your interactions with both the Agency and outside interests on a particular matter. At the beginning of the meeting, I will ask each person on the Committee to voluntarily discuss any such areas they wish to identify. . . . Issues of concern can include the extent to which you or your organization have received (or will receive) professional or personal benefits from any individuals, organizations or groups . . . representing any viewpoint concerning the issue(s) under consideration at this meeting.

Flaak Mem. at 3. At both IAQC public reviews, no one admitted representing industry or any other § 403(c) constituency.[15] This result was in accordance with SAB's designed purpose and the EPA ethics advisory sent to IAQC.

After reviewing the Radon Research Act, analyzing the SAB, and reviewing the actual composition of the IAQC, the court has found no evidence that the IAQC involved with the ETS Risk Assessment satisfied § 403(c) of the Radon Research Act. EPA's procedures, guidelines, and conduct in the ETS Risk Assessment clearly demonstrate that SAB and IAQC are independent bodies. EPA's argument that IAQC was a representative body is without merit. IAQC's membership did not include individuals from industry or representatives from more than one state. No members were invited to represent or admitted to representing any constituency. Rather, EPA's regulations prohibited parties with meaningful outside interests from participating. Accordingly, EPA failed to comply with the requirements of § 403(c).

---

[15] See 1990 IAQC Transcript at 11-38 (JA 8,803-30); 1992 IAQC Transcript at 16-29 (JA 11,655-668).

C.   The Timing of Committee Formation

EPA argues that § 403(c) is generally worded and does not make the formation of a representative advisory committee a prerequisite that must be satisfied before EPA can undertake a specific activity under the Act.   There is no evidence in the record, nor does EPA argue, that EPA established the committee during or after any activity conducted under the Act.   Since the committee has not been established, EPA's argument about when it could have sought the committee's assistance appears academic. However, for purposes of fashioning a remedy, § 403(c) requires EPA to seek the committee's assistance "in carrying out the research program . . . ." Congress intended consultation at least while EPA conducted research.   Ongoing consultation requires more than post hoc consultation.   See Morabito v. Blum, 528 F. Supp. 252, 264-66 (S.D.N.Y. 1981) (Under the Social Security Act, where consultation with a medical advisory committee is required, committee input must be sought and received before action is taken.).

D.   Consequences of EPA's Procedural Failure

Plaintiffs argue EPA's actions were unlawful and the ETS Risk Assessment must be set aside.   EPA argues Plaintiffs

30

were not prejudiced "because EPA in fact utilized extensive

public participation and peer review drawing upon all of the

designated constituencies in developing the ETS Risk Assessment."

(Conformed Mem. Supp. EPA's Cross Mot. Part. Summ. J. at 42-43.)

Further in its memorandum, however, EPA maintains it did "not

have an obligation to respond to public comments in the same

manner as in [an APA] section 553 rulemaking," id. at 49, and the

court cannot require EPA to respond to comments because

"reviewing courts are generally not free to impose additional

procedural requirements if the agencies have not chosen to grant

them." Id.

Even if EPA did provide a genuine opportunity for comment

and SAB review, the Agency was required to carry out its research

program with the assistance of an advisory group of

representatives of the identified interests. EPA may not rewrite

the terms of the Radon Research Act. See Environmental Defense

Fund, Inc. v. EPA, 636 F.2d 1267, 1283-84 (D.C. Cir. 1980)

(agency-created "de minimis" cutoff from application of statute

was struck down because not in compliance with terms of statute);

Alabama Power Co. v. Costle, 636 F.2d 323, 365 (D.C. Cir. 1979)

(The agency is not "free to ignore the plain meaning of the

statute and to substitute its policy judgment for that of

Congress."). When Congress requires specific procedures,

agencies may not ignore them or fashion substitutes.[16]

A congressional directive to consult an advisory committee

is more than a formality. The Court of Appeals for the District

of Columbia emphasized the significance of advisory committees in

explaining the procedural requirements within the Federal Coal

Mine Health and Safety Act of 1969:

> The most important aspect is the requirement of
> consultation with knowledgeable representatives of
> federal and state government, industry and labor.
> This goes far beyond the usual requirements of
> public notice and opportunity for comment set
> forth in the Administrative Procedure Act, and
> represents the Congressional answer to the fears
> expressed by industry and labor of the prospect of
> unchecked federal administrative discretion in the
> field. These rather unique requirements of the
> Act are an important part of the ultimate
> legislative compromise, and must be given their
> due weight.

---

[16] Even so, the IAQC was a poor proxy for industry
representation. EPA sought parties near the "middle" of the
spectrum when establishing SAB panels and allegedly avoided
representation from either end of the spectrum. As a general
rule, the tobacco industry occupies that end of the spectrum
contesting the carcinogenicity of ETS and EPA's motives. A
committee aspiring to represent the middle of the ETS debate
necessarily suppresses the tobacco industry's perspective.
Further, industry's ability to submit comments to a "neutral"
committee, which itself had access to EPA, is not equivalent to
industry access to EPA.

32

Zeigler Coal Co. v. Kleppe, 536 F.2d 398, 403 (D.C. Cir. 1976).

In National Constructors Ass'n v. Marshal, 581 F.2d 960 (D.C.

Cir. 1978), the Secretary of Labor was obligated to establish and

consult with a specially constituted advisory committee when

promulgating safety standards. The Secretary failed to do so.

The Marshal court rejected the agency's effort to equate notice

and comment with the required procedures and concluded that

"advisory committee consultation should, but in this case did

not, consist of something more than a . . . rest stop on the

route between a tentative proposal . . . and the final

promulgation . . . ." Id. at 971.

EPA relies on Vermont Yankee Nuclear Power Corp. v. NRDC,

435 U.S. 519, 558, 98 S. Ct. 1197, 1219, 55 L. Ed. 2d 460 (1978).

In Vermont Yankee, the agency complied with statutory procedures,

but the appeals court held the agency should have done more. The

Supreme Court reversed, noting "we find absolutely nothing in the

relevant statutes to justify what the court did here." Id. at

557, 98 S. Ct. at 1218. In the present action, EPA violated a

statutory procedure.

At issue then is the proper remedy for agency action that is

procedurally deficient. Specifically, the court must determine

whether to vacate the ETS Risk Assessment. In Vermont Yankee,

33

the Court held "[a]dministrative decisions should be set aside . . . only for substantial procedural or substantive reasons as mandated by statute . . . ." Id. at 558, 98 S. Ct. at 1219.

In Synthetic Organic Chem. Mfrs. Ass'n v. Brennan, 506 F.2d 385, 388-89 (3d Cir. 1974), Congress gave the Secretary of Labor the option of requesting recommendations from an advisory committee prior to promulgating certain rules. If the Secretary used the committee, interested parties could submit their comments about the rule after the committee issued its report. The dispute before the Third Circuit arose when the Secretary consulted the committee but published a proposed rule before the advisory committee submitted its report. The complainants "were not given adequate time to submit comments or to prepare for the hearing after the committee's work was completed." Id. at 388. The court remanded the standards to the agency with the directive to republish them and follow the procedural requirements.

In Marshal, 581 F.2d 960, the agency was required to consult an advisory committee before promulgating the disputed standards. The court found the agency greatly deviated from required procedures and agency regulations by not meaningfully consulting the committee. The court concluded that, had the agency abided by its procedural requirements, the agency may have promulgated

34

different standards. Accordingly, the court remanded the standards back to the agency for consultation with the advisory committee. Because the court also found the standards as promulgated were not illegal and the administrative record did not contain any glaring deficiencies, the court ordered a minimum remand of ninety days during which the standards would remain in effect. If the committee recommended alteration, the agency would have to reevaluate the standards.

In Brennan and Marshal, the agencies failed procedural requirements in the process of promulgating agency standards. In both Brennan and Marshal, the courts remanded the disputed agency standards with directives to comply with the procedural directives. The Marshal decision left the standards intact; the Brennan decision did not.

This case is similar to Brennan and Marshal in that the ETS Risk Assessment constitutes an agency characterization promulgated without adherence to statutory procedure. However, this case is also unique. First, it is quite clear that the ETS Risk Assessment consumed significantly more resources than the promulgation of standards in Brennan and Marshal. Second, Congress' procedural requirements in the Radon Research Act adhere to the research process. Remanding the ETS Risk

Assessment for post hoc consultation could not satisfy statutory requirements of consultation during research.

To satisfy the Radon Research Act's procedural requirements, the court would have to vacate the Assessment. EPA could then conduct research on ETS with the assistance of a representative committee. However, in <u>Vermont Yankee</u>, the Supreme Court advised that agency action should be set aside only for substantial reason. By itself, disregarding a statutory mandate to establish and consult an advisory committee is substantial. Again, EPA expended significant resources over several years in producing an assessment which claimed to deal with public health and safety. The Assessment's subject matter and EPA's expenditures raise the threshold of what constitutes a substantial reason.

EPA's complete disregard of statutory procedure and the potential waste of significant executive branch resources dealing with health and safety each suggest a different remedy. In resolving this conflict, the court finds persuasive the rationale underlying the District of Columbia's remedy in <u>Marshal</u>. In addition to enforcing Congress' directive, the remedy should ameliorate the harm caused, or being caused, by EPA's procedural violation.[17] The court is reluctant to characterize EPA's procedural deficiency substantial where EPA would simply reproduce the same ETS Risk Assessment at significant cost. In resolving the substantiality of EPA's procedural defect, the court must inquire whether EPA's procedural failure affected the Assessment. See Textile Workers Union of America v. Lincoln Mills of Alabama, 353 U.S. 448, 457, 77 S. Ct. 912, 918 (1957) (Some federal law "lack[s] express statutory sanction but will be solved by looking at the policy of the legislation and fashioning a remedy that will effectuate that policy. The range of judicial inventiveness will be determined by the nature of the problem."); United States v. Field, 193 F.2d 92, 96 (2nd Cir. 1951) ("'[I]t is fundamental that federal courts, in common with other courts, have inherent power to do all things that are reasonably necessary for the administration of justice, within the scope of their jurisdiction.'")

-----

[17] In deciding whether procedural compliance could have produced a different outcome, the Marshal decision also distinguished agency action that violated the law. EPA's procedural failure constitutes a violation of the law. Where significant agency resources are at stake, the court will not, however, adopt a formal, bright line rule.

V.   THE ENVIRONMENTAL TOBACCO SMOKE RISK ASSESSMENT

A.   Overview

The court reviews the performance of the ETS Risk
Assessment to determine whether consultation with the
representative group would have likely produced a different
result.[18]   The court also reviews the record to determine whether
EPA conducted the Assessment in accordance with the Radon
Research Act, aside from procedural defects.   Plaintiffs contest
the validity of Chapters 3, 4, and 5 of the final ETS Risk
Assessment.   A brief overview of the Assessment will elucidate
the arguments.[19]

Chapter 1 summarizes the claim that ETS is a Group A
carcinogen that causes approximately 3,000 lung cancer deaths per

---

[18]   Plaintiffs initially argue that had industry been
consulted during the research process, EPA likely would not have
conducted a risk assessment and carcinogen classification.
Plaintiffs' argument depends on the ETS Risk Assessment being
ultra vires.   As already addressed, risk assessment is incidental
to gathering information, researching, and disseminating the
findings.

[19]   The parties' arguments to the court address whether
EPA's conduct was arbitrary and capricious and whether the record
demonstrates reasoned decision making.   The court uses the
arguments to determine whether the Assessment would have been
different had industry (and state) representatives addressed
their concerns directly to EPA.   The inquiry turns on the
legitimacy of Plaintiffs' concerns.

year among nonsmokers. Chapter 2 provides an introduction and overview. EPA states the study was conducted in accordance with its Risk Assessment Guidelines. The report explains EPA did not use its Guidelines for Health and Risk Assessment of Chemical Mixtures because mainstream smoke (MS)[20] and ETS are not sufficiently similar. Specifically, using "cigarette-equivalents" to correlate ETS exposure was not conducted for several reasons.

> Although MS and ETS are qualitatively similar with respect to chemical composition (i.e., they contain most, if not all, of the same toxicants and carcinogens), the absolute and proportional quantities of the components, as well as their physical state, can differ substantially. . . . Furthermore, it is not known which of the chemicals in tobacco smoke are responsible for its carcinogenicity. Clearly, the comparison of a small number of biomarker measures cannot adequately quantify differential distributions of unknown carcinogenic compounds.
>
> Another area of uncertainty in the "cigarette-equivalents" approach relates to potential metabolic differences between active and passive smokers. . . . Because of these uncertainties, the data from active smoking are more appropriate for qualitative hazard identification than for quantitative dose-response assessment.

---

[20] Mainstream smoke is the smoke inhaled by the smoker.

ETS Risk Assessment at 2-7 thru 2-8. The report then states that although ETS and MS are chemically similar, "ETS is rapidly diluted into the environment, and consequently, passive smokers are exposed to much lower concentrations of these agents than are active smokers." Id. at 2-8.

Chapter 3 establishes that ETS and MS are chemically similar because: (a) ETS is composed of aged, diluted sidestream smoke (SS),[21] and aged, diluted, exhaled MS, and (b) fifty-two of the 4,000+ characterized chemical constituents of MS were found in SS, which include most of the suspected carcinogens identified in MS.

Chapter 4 states that the high relative risks (RR) for lung cancer associated with active smoking along "with no evidence of a threshold level of exposure," id. at 2-9, the chemical similarity between MS and ETS, and corroborative evidence for the carcinogenicity of tobacco smoke provided by animal bioassay and genotoxicity studies "clearly establish the biological plausibility that ETS is also a human lung carcinogen." Id. at 2-9; see also 4-27 thru 4-29. EPA asserts these observations

_____

[21] Sidestream smoke is the smoke emitted from a smoldering cigarette between puffs.

alone are sufficient to establish ETS as a Group A carcinogen designation.[22]

Chapter 4 concludes with recognition that EPA should examine the "vast body of epidemiologic data dealing specifically with lung cancer and exposure to ETS." Id. at 4-29. The chapter concludes this data should be examined: (1) to promote "the interest of weighing all the available evidence, as recommended by EPA's [Risk Assessment Guidelines] . . ." (2) because SS and MS rapidly dilute into the environment and ETS components change phase distributions over time, which raises questions about the carcinogenicity of ETS exposure under environmental conditions, and (3) since "active smoking data do not constitute a good basis for quantitative estimation of the health effects of passive

---

[22] A substance is categorized as a Group A Human Carcinogen "only when there is sufficient evidence from epidemiologic studies to support a causal association between exposure to the agents and cancer." Risk Assessment Guidelines at 34,000.

> Three criteria must be met before a causal association can be inferred between exposure and cancer in humans: 1. There is no identified bias that could explain the association. 2. The possibility of confounding has been considered and ruled out as explaining the association. 3. The association is unlikely to be due to chance.

Id. at 33,999.

smoking because the relative uptake and deposition between active and passive smokers of the agent(s) responsible for these effects are not known . . . ." Id.

Chapter 5 analyzes thirty-one epidemiologic studies of nonsmoking women married to smoking spouses (spousal smoking studies). Chapter 5 combines the spousal smoking studies data into six statistical "meta-analysis" based on geographic origin. Chapter 5 also analyzes high-exposure groups in the studies, conducts a trend analysis, and categorizes studies into four tiers based on their perceived utility for assessing an ETS/lung cancer association. The analysis within Chapter 5 utilizes one-tailed tests of significance and 90% confidence intervals. "The justification for this usage is based on the a priori hypothesis [from the theory of biological plausibility] that a positive association exists between exposure to ETS and lung cancer." Id. at 5-2.

Chapter 6 conducts an exposure assessment in an attempt to quantify the threat posed by ETS. Chapter 6 concludes that MS and ETS are too dissimilar to use data about MS to assess the risks of ETS exposure. Id. at 6-6. Chapter 6 thus bases its exposure assessment on data from the spousal smoking studies and asserts that ETS exposure causes approximately 3,000 nonsmoker lung cancer deaths each year.[23]

The Addendum addresses large U.S. spousal smoking studies published in 1992. It claims "these new studies are generally consistent with this report's conclusions . . . ." *Id.* at ADD-1. Appendix A reviews the thirty-one spousal smoking studies and explains how the studies were assigned to tiers based on their perceived utility. Appendix B explains how EPA adjusted the data used in Chapter 5's meta-analysis to address the effects of smoker misclassification bias.

There are two issues. The first is whether EPA's consulting a representative committee, on which industry's concerns were represented during the research process, likely would have caused EPA to change the conduct or conclusions of its ETS assessment. The key to this determination is whether industry representatives could have presented meritable criticism and advice. The second issue is whether EPA's conduct was otherwise in accordance with the Radon Research Act.

---

[23] Chapters 7 and 8 do not involve the carcinogenicity of ETS.

B.   Biological Plausibility

1.   Industry Criticism

Plaintiffs argue EPA's "biological plausibility" analysis is flawed because the Agency disregarded evidence that MS and ETS are not similar, failed to identify the criteria used in equating MS and ETS, and disregarded evidence that MS has a no-effect threshold. The importance of Plaintiffs' arguments is that the biological plausibility analysis establishes Chapter 5's "a priori hypothesis" that ETS is a Group A carcinogen. EPA uses this hypothesis to justify the use of one-tailed significance tests, which the Agency in turn relies upon to switch from a 95% to 90% confidence interval.

Plaintiffs assert the record does not explain why EPA ignored record evidence and EPA's own findings in the chemical similarity analysis of Chapter 3. Plaintiffs point out that EPA analyzed the similarity of MS and ETS three times and reached three different conclusions. Chapter 6 establishes ETS and MS were too dissimilar to use MS data to establish the carcinogenic risk of ETS, and Chapter 2 states the similarity of ETS to MS was too indeterminate to assess risk according to EPA's Guidelines for the Health Risk Assessment of Chemical Mixtures. Chapter 3, however, uses the chemical similarities of ETS and MS to

44

establish ETS as a known human carcinogen. Plaintiffs argue

Chapter 3's similarity analysis fails for three reasons: (1) the

chapter ignored Assessment findings about the differences between

MS and ETS; (2) EPA ignored evidence rejecting any chemical

similarity; and (3) EPA did not define the criteria used to reach

conclusions about the similarity/dissimilarity/indeterminacy of

MS and ETS.

Plaintiffs point out Chapter 3's similarity analysis is

contradicted by the explanation at the end of Chapter 4 for

analyzing epidemiologic data. Specifically, "[t]he rapid

dilution of both SS and exhaled MS into the environment and

changing phase distributions of ETS components over time raise

some questions about the carcinogenic potential of ETS under

actual environmental exposure conditions." ETS Risk Assessment

at 4-29.

In rejecting using a "cigarette-equivalents" correlation,

Chapter 2 states that although MS and ETS are qualitatively

similar, the absolute and proportional quantities of the

components, as well as their physical state, differ

substantially. EPA also rejects this equivalents analysis

because it does not know which tobacco smoke chemicals cause

cancer nor the effect metabolic differences between active and passive smokers have on carcinogenicity. <u>See</u> <u>id.</u> at 2-7 thru

2-9. Chapter 6 bases its rejection of an equivalents analysis on

the differences between MS and SS:

> The basic assumption of cigarette-equivalents
> procedures is that the lung cancer risks in
> passive and active smokers are equivalently
> indexed by the common measure of exposure to
> tobacco smoke, i.e., a common value of the
> surrogate measure of exposure in an active and a
> passive smoker would imply the same lung cancer
> risk in both. This assumption may not be tenable,
> however, as MS and SS differ in the relative
> composition of carcinogens and other components
> identified in tobacco smoke and in their
> physicochemical properties in general; the lung
> and systemic distribution of chemical agents
> common to MS and SS are affected by their relative
> distribution between the vapor and particle
> phases, which differs between MS and SS and
> changes with SS as it ages. Active and passive
> smoking also differ in characteristics of intake
> . . . which may affect deposition and systemic
> distribution of various tobacco smoke components
> as well.

<u>Id.</u> at 6-6. EPA further revealed that such differences affect

carcinogenicity: "Pipe and cigar smokers, who inhale less deeply

than cigarette smokers, have lower risks of lung cancer than

cigarette smokers." <u>Id.</u> at 4-10.

In a draft response to comments, Kenneth Brown, the primary

author of Chapters 5 and 6, and Appendices C and D, rejects using

a cigarette-equivalents analysis because "there are differences

between active and passive smoking that may affect carcinogenic

46

risk that are not fully understood." Kenneth G. Brown, Draft

Report _Responses to Public Comments on the First EPA Draft Risk_

Assessment of ETS with Discussion of Revisions that Appear in the

Second Draft Report, Response To Comment 3.1.4, at 16 (June 1992)

(JA 6,457) (Draft Responses). The author agrees "that active and

passive smoking are vastly dissimilar with regard to exposure,"

_id._, and states,

> [a]lthough it would be of interest to know more
> about the physicochemical properties of ETS, the
> distribution of exposure concentration, exposure
> duration, and other characteristics, these things
> do not need to be fully understood to conclude
> that ETS is a carcinogen. . . . If the unknown
> characteristics regarding the properties of ETS or
> exposure to ETS nullified the carcinogenic
> potential in fresh sidestream smoke, then we would
> not expect to see an association of ETS exposure
> with increased lung cancer, as the study data
> indicate.

_Id._, Response To 3.1.2, at 14 (JA 6,455).

Plaintiffs assert EPA's statements impact EPA's biological

plausibility analysis. Regarding EPA's _a priori_ hypothesis,

Plaintiffs conclude: (1) ETS cannot be a known carcinogen if

dilution and aging raise unresolved questions about its potential

carcinogenicity, and (2) ETS and MS are not "sufficiently

similar" carcinogens if they are "vastly dissimilar" as to

exposure.

47

Plaintiffs next point to comments submitted by scientists[24] and by the tobacco industry citing scientific literature[25] that reject EPA's similarity conclusions. Plaintiffs contend EPA selectively cites or ignores certain studies, depending on whether the Agency is explaining or disclaiming similarities between ETS and MS. Plaintiffs also point out that none of the eleven U.S. epidemiologic studies analyzed in the ETS Risk Assessment, as reported by their authors, shows an overall statistically significant association between ETS and lung cancer.

Plaintiffs also argue EPA failed to identify the criteria used to determine chemical similarity. Plaintiffs insist the criteria EPA used to analyze similarity must be precise for two reasons. First, at different times in the same ETS Risk Assessment, EPA concluded that MS and ETS are similar,

----

[24] See, e.g., Comments of Cronan (JA 6,188); Comments of Gori (JA 10,839); Comments of Todhunter (JA 10,072); Comments of Flamm (JA 10,633-34); Comments of Newell (JA 10,660-61); Comments of Reasor (JA 10,786).

[25] See, e.g., Comments of The Tobacco Institute (JA 9,537-38, 9,543); Comments of Reasor (JA 10,789-90); Comments of R.J. Reynolds (JA 5,841-58); Comments of Philip Morris (JA 10,012, 10,024).

dissimilar, and of indeterminate similarity.[26] Second, EPA's

chemical similarity analysis is inconsistent with the Agency's

prior risk assessment practices. See Risk Assessment Guidelines

at 33,992 (listing "consistency of carcinogen risk assessments"

as an EPA goal). Plaintiffs then provide evidence that,

previously, EPA did not classify agents in Group A because they

contain the same constituents as other Group A carcinogens. See

Tennessee Gas Pipelines Co. v. F.E.R.C., 926 F.2d 1206, 1211

(D.C. Cir. 1991) (When an agency decision is inconsistent with

prior decisions, it must explain the change.).

As their final argument against EPA's biological

plausibility hypothesis, Plaintiffs dispute EPA's conclusion that

ETS exposure causes lung cancer because "[a] clear dose-response

relationship exists between lung cancer and amount of exposure

[to MS], without any evidence of a threshold level." ETS Risk

Assessment at 4-1. EPA's "no threshold" finding means EPA

---

[26] See Dithiocarbamate Task Force v. EPA, 98 F.3d 1394,
1404-05 (D.C. Cir. 1996) (vacating EPA's listing of a carbamate
as a "K waste" because EPA could not employ a highly
discretionary and unarticulated "environmental concern" standard
and then fail to explain why that carbamate failed to meet that
standard); see also Toler v. Eastern Assoc. Coal Co., 43 F.3d
109, 115-16 (4th Cir. 1995) (review of denial of medical
benefits, requiring an ALJ to identify specific and persuasive
reasons to justify seemingly paradoxical reasoning).

purported to find no concentration level at which MS ceases to be carcinogenic. This finding was critical because Plaintiffs assert that nonsmokers are exposed to only minute concentrations of ETS. If EPA had found a threshold for exposure to MS, then one would have to be established for ETS. Evidence of an MS exposure threshold would jeopardize EPA's biological plausibility analysis since ETS is substantially more dilute than MS. Plaintiffs point to comments and evidence in the record of thresholds in human, animal, and genotoxicity studies. Again, Plaintiffs point to EPA's selective use of studies and failure to consider or respond to contrary evidence.

2. EPA's Response

In response to Plaintiffs' claim that EPA failed to respond to certain public comments, EPA asserts that it did not have an obligation to respond to public comments in the same manner as in formal rulemaking. EPA further reminds that it is not the province of the court to impose additional procedural requirements outside those mandated by Congress.

In assessing the health risk of ETS, EPA claims it used a "total weight of the evidence" approach, see Risk Assessment Guidelines at 33,996, 33,999-34,000, and the Agency's conclusions

50

rely upon all of the available evidence, not on any single

analysis or theory. EPA offers two reasons the ETS Risk

Assessment is unique. First, the database of evidence concerning

ETS is large and derived from human data. "The use of human

evidence eliminates the uncertainties that normally arise when

one has to base hazard identification on the results of high-dose

animal experiments." ETS Risk Assessment at 2-7. Second, the

evidence consists of exposure at environmental levels people are

exposed to in everyday life. EPA states such data are rare in

risk assessments and obviate the need to extrapolate a response

from high to low exposures. The available data being unique, EPA

asserts "the guidelines themselves stress that risk analysis is

not subject to hard and fast rules, but rather must be 'conducted

on a case-by-case basis, giving consideration to all relevant

scientific information.'" (Conformed Mem. Supp. EPA's Cross Mot.

Part. Summ. J. at 47; quoting Risk Assessment Guidelines at

33,992.)

EPA explains that its biological plausibility findings rest

on three considerations. First, active smoking causes lung

cancer in humans, and MS is chemically similar to ETS. Second,

considerable evidence exists that nonsmokers exposed to ETS

absorb and metabolize significant amounts of ETS, including

51

carcinogenic compounds. Third, laboratory studies show ETS can cause cancer in animals and damage DNA, which scientists recognize as being an instrumental mechanism for cancer development. Further, EPA argues that its bioplausibility theory alone need not be sufficient to support the Assessment's conclusion, because the theory is confirmed by the findings from the epidemiologic studies.

EPA defends its Chapter 3 findings of chemical similarity by stating the Agency never suggested ETS and MS are identical compounds. Rather, EPA found that ETS and MS are similar in some respects and can be compared in terms of carcinogenicity. Differences between the compounds were not disregarded by the Agency. EPA cites to the many portions in the ETS Risk Assessment where EPA discusses the dissimilarities between MS and ETS.[27]

---

[27] EPA also relies upon IAQC's finding:

There are substantial differences in the relative composition of the smoke formed between mainstream and sidestream smoke, . . . but there is no reason to suppose that the qualitative toxicities of ETS and MS are substantively different. In comparing these two agents the differences are largely ones of dose and duration of exposure rather than fundamental differences in the toxicity or carcinogenicity of the agent in question.

(continued...)

EPA asserts the Assessment specifically discusses dilution in ambient air, aging, and exposure characteristics. Review of EPA's citations reveals very limited discussion. The discussions primarily admit that these are areas of uncertainty. See ETS Risk Assessment at 3-10 ("Detailed chemical characterizations of ETS emissions . . . are limited. As a result, the impact on ETS of factors such as the rapid dilution of SS emissions, adsorption and remission of contaminants, and exhaled MS is not well understood."); see also id. at 3-12 (ETS concentration is the result of a complex interaction of at least 13 variables; studies show large variations in contaminant concentrations.). EPA asserts that despite these uncertainties, nonsmokers' lungs are nevertheless exposed to and absorb contaminants, including carcinogens, and that exposure can be at significant levels relative to active smokers.

EPA characterizes Plaintiffs' contrasting the Agency's differing conclusions on ETS-MS similarities as nothing more than obfuscating the differences between qualitative and quantitative assessments. EPA claims the first issue (hazard identification)

_____

[27](...continued)
EPA, An SAB Report: Review of Draft Passive Smoking Health Effects Document, EPA/SAB/IAQC/93/003, at 11, November 20, 1992.

in the risk assessment process is a qualitative determination as to whether a substance is carcinogenic. See Risk Assessment Guidelines at 33,993 ("The hazard identification component qualitatively answers the question of how likely an agent is to be a human carcinogen."). EPA asserts that if the substance is identified as a hazard, the second question is a quantitative assessment as to how dangerous a carcinogenic substance is to humans. See id. (Quantitative risk assessment is a general term to describe all or parts of dose-response assessment, exposure assessment, and risk characterization.).

EPA also claims it explained four criteria for finding MS and ETS chemically similar: (1) the process resulting in the generation of MS and SS; (2) the identity of toxins and carcinogens in the two substances; (3) the relative toxicity and carcinogenicity of SS and MS per cigarette smoke; and (4) the demonstrated exposure to and absorption by the body of significant levels of carcinogens and other toxins. In response to the charge that it changed its approach in evaluating biological plausibility vis-a-vis other Group A carcinogen determinations, EPA states risk assessments are conducted on a case-by-case basis. Thus, comparison to other EPA Group A determinations are not relevant. EPA then re-explains the basis

54

for its plausibility hypothesis and states no other EPA Group A determination involves comparison with a substance whose carcinogenicity is as potent and as well documented as MS.

EPA asserts the epidemiologic studies reviewed in Chapter 4 establish MS as a human carcinogen. In defense of chemical similarity, EPA recites the similarities between SS and MS. Both compounds contain the same carcinogenic compounds, moreover, EPA asserts "there is voluminous record evidence demonstrating that SS is more toxic per cigarette smoked than the carcinogenic MS." (Conformed Mem. Supp. EPA's Cross Mot. Part. Summ. J. at 62.)

In recognizing that ETS is rapidly diluted into the environment, EPA explains that it analyzed the extent to which nonsmokers actually absorb and metabolize ETS. First, EPA examined the extent of nonsmokers' actual exposure to ETS in a variety of indoor environments. The studies EPA reviewed showed measurable carcinogens and toxins in ETS at levels that varied but consistently exceeded background levels. Second, EPA reviewed biomarker studies which showed at least some of the carcinogens in ETS are absorbed by the body at a higher rate than nicotine. The human carcinogen 4-aminobiphenyl (4-ABP), which is emitted at concentrations 31 times greater in SS than MS, was present in the blood of nonsmokers exposed to ETS in

55

concentrations of one-tenth to one-fifth of that found in active smokers. These studies lead EPA to conclude that nonsmokers exposed to ETS absorb and metabolize ETS, including carcinogenic compounds.

EPA asserts that Plaintiffs' arguments are simply attacks on the uncertainties inherent in the risk assessment process. A risk assessment, by its very nature, is not a final determination about the health effects of a substance but is instead an assessment that makes the best judgments possible based upon the available evidence. Ethyl Corp. v. EPA, 541 F.2d 1, 24 (D.C. Cir. 1976). In conducting risk assessments, an agency must adopt inference options and point out where evidence and scientific knowledge are incomplete. NRC Redbook, at 18, 28.

Finally, EPA defends its determination that there is no safe level of exposure to MS by referring to several studies that found a risk of lung cancer at the lowest levels of exposure to MS. EPA also relies upon SAB's finding it plausible that prolonged inhalation of ETS results in some increase of lung cancer. Finally, EPA asserts the record rebuts Plaintiffs' argument that nonsmokers are exposed only to small amounts of ETS.

56

3. Analysis

EPA offers three assertions as the foundation for its biological plausibility hypothesis. Plaintiffs contest EPA's first assertion that MS and ETS are similar. In support of its second assertion, EPA points to evidence in the record that some components of ETS are absorbed by nonsmokers. EPA does not, however, direct the court to evidence in the record demonstrating that the observed absorption of ETS constituents answers the questions of carcinogenicity raised elsewhere in EPA's analysis.

There is limited evidence in the record supporting EPA's final basis for its plausibility hypothesis. The animal laboratory studies used by EPA present some evidence supporting EPA's hypothesis. EPA conducted no animal lifetime inhalation studies of ETS but did conduct cigarette smoke inhalation studies on Syrian golden hamsters. The studies detected no evidence of lung cancer but did detect evidence of cancer of the upper larynx and a dose-response relationship. The record does not state whether the substance analyzed, air-diluted cigarette smoke (1:15), replicated MS, SS, or ETS. The remaining studies, upon which EPA relies, involve analysis of SS condensates from smoking machines. The Assessment does not explain, nor does EPA direct the court to any evidence within the record explaining, how SS condensate demonstrates similarities between MS and ETS.

The court is disturbed that EPA and Kenneth Brown buttress the bioplausibility theory with the epidemiology studies. EPA's theory must be independently plausible. EPA relied upon similarities between MS and ETS to conclude that it is biologically plausible that ETS causes cancer. EPA terms this theory its "<u>a priori</u> hypothesis" in justifying Chapter 5's methodology. Chapter 5's methodology allowed EPA to demonstrate a statistically significant association between ETS exposure and lung cancer. <u>See</u> Federal Judicial Center, <u>Reference Manual on Scientific Evidence</u> 154-55, (1994) (Narrowing the confidence intervals makes it more likely that a study will be found to be statistically significant.). Chapter 5's analysis rests on the validity of the biological plausibility theory. It is circular for EPA to now argue the epidemiology studies support the Agency's <u>a priori</u> theory. Without the theory, the studies would likely have done no such thing.

The record also does not support EPA's argument that contrasting EPA's three positions on ETS-MS similarities constitutes obfuscation. EPA's Risk Assessment Guidelines establish a distinction between qualitative and quantitative

58

analysis. However, for purposes of EPA's bioplausibility theory, neither the ETS Risk Assessment or administrative record demonstrates a difference or attempt the explanation which EPA now offers the court. Quantity versus quality may be a relevant distinction in certain situations, e.g., the amount of arsenic naturally occurring in an apple. Plaintiffs assert that since ETS is a gas, considering the evidence regarding ETS' physicochemical properties and the characteristics of the particles and gases comprising ETS is necessary to determine the quality of ETS. This suggests an analytical process combining qualitative and quantitative analysis, which is also what EPA's Risk Assessment Guidelines suggest.

EPA's Risk Assessment Guidelines do not support the Agency's argument that risk assessment is a bifurcated, quantitative then qualitative, analysis. To the contrary, "[r]isk assessment includes one or more of the following components: hazard identification, dose-response assessment, exposure assessment, and risk characterization (NRC 1983)." Risk Assessment Guidelines at 33,993 (emphasis added). "[Q]uantitative risk assessment has been used as an inclusive term to describe all or parts of dose-response assessment, exposure assessment, and risk characterization. . . . [However,] the more explicit terminology

59

developed by the NRC (1983) is usually preferred." Id. Neither

the Assessment or the administrative record explains why

physicochemical inquiries require a bifurcated analysis instead

of a combined analysis as per the Guidelines, or why MS and ETS

are similar for purposes of hazard identification, but not for

purposes of quantitative risk assessments. Since Chapter 2 found

ETS and MS not sufficiently similar, Chapter 3 found them

similar, and Chapter 6 found them dissimilar, EPA apparently used

a different risk assessment methodology for each chapter. Again,

neither the Assessment nor the record explains the risk

assessment components used in the different chapters, why

methodologies varied between chapters, or why ETS and MS were or

were not similar using each methodology.

The court is faced with the ugly possibility that EPA

adopted a methodology for each chapter, without explanation,

based on the outcome sought in that chapter. This possibility is

most potent where EPA rejected MS-ETS similarities to avoid a

"cigarette-equivalents" analysis in determining carcinogenicity

of ETS exposure. Use of cigarette-equivalents analysis may have

lead to a conclusion that ETS is not a Group A carcinogen.[28]   It

_____

[28]   [S]ome persons suggest a dosimetric approach
(continued...)

is striking that MS and ETS were similar only where such a conclusion promoted finding ETS a carcinogen.

EPA's assertion that "EPA did explain the numerous criteria it used in assessing similarity . . . ," (Conformed Mem. Supp. EPA's Cross Mot. Part. Summ. J. at 73), is without merit. EPA merely parrots the findings made in Chapter 3 of the ETS Risk Assessment. The record presents no evidence of EPA establishing similarity criteria before the Assessment.[29] Nor did the

---

[28] (...continued)
(called "cigarette-equivalents" in the Report) to estimate lung cancer risk from ETS exposure from data on active smoking. An average ETS exposure is determined to be equivalent to actively smoking some percentage of one cigarette per day. Extrapolating downward on a does-response [sic] curve for active smoking at that level suggests a "negligible" lung cancer risk.

Kenneth G. Brown, Draft Report Responses to Public Comments on the First EPA Draft Risk Assessment of ETS with Discussion of Revisions that Appear in the Second Draft Report, Comment 3.1.4, at 15 (June 25, 1992) (JA 6,456) (Draft Responses). Dr. Brown's response does not rebut the asserted consequences of a cigarette equivalents analysis.

[29] See Portland Cement Ass'n v. Ruckelshaus, 486 F.2d 375, 395 (D.C. Cir. 1973) ("A troublesome aspect of this case is the identification of what, in fact, formed the basis for the standards promulgated by EPA - a question that must be probed prior to consideration of whether the basis or bases for the standards is reliable."); see also Independent U.S. Tanker Owners Comm. v. Lewis, 690 F.2d 908, 920 (D.C. Cir. 1982) (noting that when agency action is undertaken prior to disclosure of the basis
(continued...)

scientists on IAQC's final review panel identify the criteria used to determine similarity.[30] EPA's citations reveal only summaries of findings on MS-SS similarities and ETS biomarkers.[31]

---

[29](...continued)
of the action, "[t]here is an overwhelming institutional bias in favor of justifying the result in any way possible.")

[30] The data in Chapter 3 "do not . . . adequately support the conclusion that the two are chemically similar. . . . [T]he data that are in there, speaking as a chemist, they simply don't make the case." 1992 IAQC Review at II-41 (Dr. Daisey) (JA 11,969). "That also brings you to an issue of what you mean by 'chemically similar,' which is not so simple to discuss. . . . [P]erhaps we don't have to consider it. But in a broader sense, the chapter often talks about sort, of vague quantitative terms . . . ." Id. at II-43 (JA 11,971). "What does it mean? What is the test for chemical similarity?" Id. at II-51 (Dr. Hammond) (JA 11,979). "[T]he data . . . simply do not demonstrate that they are similar. There are simply not enough data. . . . [Y]ou're not going to have that data, and even if you did, you'd have to decide on criteria for what constitutes similarity and what does not constitute similarity." Id. at II-77 (Dr. Daisey) (JA 12,005).

[31] Instead of explaining the criteria used to make findings, EPA's citations reveal more uncertainty. "Standardized testing protocols for assessing the physical and chemical nature of SS emissions . . . do not exist, and data on SS are not as extensive as those for MS emissions." ETS Risk Assessment at 3-2.

> Although ETS is a major source of indoor air contaminants, the actual contribution of ETS to indoor air is difficult to assess due to the background levels of many contaminants contribute from a variety of other indoor and outdoor sources. Relatively few of the individual constituents of the ETS mix have been identified and characterized. In addition, little is known about the role of individual ETS constituents in
> (continued...)

The record does not support EPA's arguments that EPA took MS-ETS differences into account and, despite them, concluded ETS is a known human carcinogen because nonsmokers are exposed to and absorb carcinogens. EPA conceded that dilution, aging, and exposure characteristics fundamentally distinguish ETS from mainstream smoke, and "raise . . . questions about the carcinogenic potential of ETS." ETS Risk Assessment at 2-7 thru 2-8, 4-29, 6-6. See also Draft Responses at 14-16 (JA 6,455-57). The record does not explain how, after raising these questions, EPA could classify ETS a known human carcinogen based on similarities between SS and MS. The record also fails to explain whether or how EPA determined that, because some components of ETS may be absorbed, questions raised in other areas of the assessment about the carcinogenic potential of ETS were no longer relevant.

Finally, both sides cite to independent studies on ETS, done by third parties, to support their arguments. Both sides often lay claim to the same studies. The studies predominantly contain

_____

[31](...continued)
eliciting the adverse health and nuisance effects observed.

Id. at 3-18.

information useful to both sides, and often conflict with one another. The court finds one review particularly relevant, a review conducted within EPA on the ETS Risk Assessment. EPA's Risk Criteria Office, a group of EPA risk assessment experts, concluded that EPA failed to reasonably explain how all relevant data on ETS, evaluated according to EPA Risk Assessment Guidelines' causality criteria, can support a Group A classification. Acting Director Chris DeRosa advised EPA that the evidence "support[ed] the conclusion that ETS be classified as a Group B1 carcinogen."[32] EPA Toxicologist Larry Glass concluded, "it is recommended that the [epidemiological] evidence be summarized as being _limited_ . . . . This would classify ETS into a weight-of-the-evidence Group B1."[33] Office Director Terry Harvey also concluded that the ETS Classification's analysis violated EPA's Risk Assessment Guidelines: "[l]ike it or not,

---

[32] EPA Memorandum from Chris DeRosa, Acting Director Environmental Criteria and Assessment Office, to William H. Farland, Director, Office of Health and Environmental Assessment (OHEA) 1 (April 27, 1990) (JA 6,651).

[33] _Id._ at 4-5 (JA 6,654-55). The same author recognizes "tremendous scientific, regulatory, and political ramifications of categorizing a substance as a Group A carcinogen. . . . [G]iven the inherent limitations of the data, and the comparative novelty of the approach used to interpret the data I would recommend that this approach not be used as the basis of a Group A classification." _Id._ at 4 (JA 6,654).

EPA should live within its own categorization framework or clearly explain why we chose not to do so."[34]

In summary, Plaintiffs raise legitimate questions not addressed in the record regarding EPA's bioplausibility theory. If confronted by a representative committee that voiced industry concerns, EPA would likely have had to resolve these issues in the record. It is not clear whether EPA could have or can do so. These issues are more than periphery. If EPA's a priori hypothesis fails, EPA has no justification for manipulating the Agency's standard scientific methodology.

C. EPA's Choice of Epidemiological Studies

By the time EPA released the ETS Risk Assessment in 1993, 33 studies had analyzed the lung cancer risk of nonsmoking females married to smoking spouses, 12 studies had analyzed the risk of females exposed to ETS in the workplace, and 13 studies had analyzed the risk of females exposed to ETS in childhood. Six of the 58 analyses (10.3%) reported a statistically significant association between ETS exposure and lung cancer for

---

[34] EPA Memorandum from Terry Harvey, Director, Environmental Criteria and Assessment Office, to Linda Bailey, Technical Information Staff, OHEA 2 (March 24, 1992) (emphasis added) (JA 6,661).

nonsmoking females; two of 13 analyses for male nonsmokers were significant. EPA chose 31 of the 33 studies done on nonsmoking females married to smoking spouses. Of the 33 studies completed in 1993, three large U.S. studies were not completed at the time EPA conducted its second IAQC review. EPA used interim results from one of the three, the Fontham study, and did not include the other two in its overall assessment. EPA did not draw its conclusions directly from the 31 studies it chose. Instead, EPA pooled the results of the studies and arranged the data into categories by geographic region and exposure level. EPA then organized and analyzed the studies by the quality of their methodology. This technique of synthesizing findings across related studies is known as meta-analysis.

The Risk Assessment gives short notice to why the childhood or workplace studies were not evaluated. The assessment states,

> [t]he use of a more homogenous group allows more
> confidence in the results of combined study
> analyses. . . . Some [studies] also provide
> information on childhood and/or workplace
> exposure, but there is far less information on
> these exposures; therefore, in order to develop
> one large database for analysis, only the female
> exposures from spousal smoking are considered.

ETS Risk Assessment at 5-1. The Assessment's overview explains only that childhood and workplace studies are fewer, represent

fewer cases, and are generally excluded from EPA's analysis. Id.
at 1-8. The Addendum mentions the two large U.S. female
nonsmoker studies but does not explain why the two were excluded
but the Fontham study included.

In its first review, IAQC stated that one of four criteria
necessary to conduct a meta-analysis is a "precise definition of
criteria used to include (or exclude) studies." EPA, An SAB
Report: Review of Draft Environmental Tobacco Smoke Health
Effects Document, EPA/SAB/IAQC/91/007 at 32-33 (1991) (SAB 1991
Review) (JA 9,497-98). Regarding the studies chosen for the ETS
Risk Assessment, IAQC stated,

> [s]pecific criteria for including studies was not
> provided. The importance of this was reinforced
> at the Committee meeting when a reanalysis was
> presented on a different set of studies than those
> in the report. This resulted in a change in the
> overall risk estimate. Decisions as to study
> inclusion should be made prior to analysis, based
> on clearly stated criteria. It is also desirable
> to evaluate the impact on conclusions of closely
> related, but excluded, studies.

Id. at 33 (first emphasis added) (JA 9,498). In its 1992 review,
neither EPA or IAQC addressed again the criteria used to
determine which studies were included in the meta-analysis. IAQC
stated that the combination of studies used provided a
scientifically defensible basis for estimating the relative risk

67

of lung cancer associated with ETS among American women who have never smoked cigarettes. IAQC also supported EPA's general meta-analysis categorization of the studies which EPA had chosen. See EPA, An SAB Report: Review of Draft Passive Smoking Health Effects Document, EPA/SAB/IAQC/93/003 at 3-4, 22 (1992) (IAQC review which EPA now misrepresents as a full explanation of EPA's database choice with express IAQC support) (JA 12,207-08, 12,226).

Plaintiffs contest that EPA excluded studies and data on workplace and childhood exposure to ETS, as well as the "two largest and most recent" U.S. spousal smoking studies, because inclusion would have undermined EPA's claim of a causal association between ETS exposure and lung cancer.[35] (Conformed Mem. Supp. Pls.' Mot. Summ. J. at 66.) In its memorandum before this court, EPA offers four reasons for excluding the workplace and childhood data.

"First, such data are less extensive and therefore less reliable." (Conformed Mem. Supp. EPA's Cross Mot. Part. Summ. J. at 88.) EPA's three citations to the record do not support this

---

[35] Plaintiffs also argue EPA included workplace data that affirmed the Agency's a priori hypothesis. The court does not find it necessary to reach the merits of this assertion.

assertion. All three citations state there is less information in the disputed studies. One of Dr. Brown's draft responses also calls the disputed studies inadequate, without reason or explanation. IAQC also recognized the disputed studies contained less information, however, IAQC concluded "the report should review and comment on the data that do exist . . . ." SAB 1991 Review at 5 (JA 9,470). The court has also found no record support or reason for the assertion that smaller studies are less reliable for purposes of meta-analysis. The purpose of meta-analysis is utilization of smaller studies.

Similarly, EPA's second assertion that workplace studies were excluded because of potential confounders is without record support. As evidence explaining why EPA excluded workplace studies from the meta-analysis, EPA cites IAQC's 1991 Review discussing limitations on EPA's reliance on spousal smoking as an indicator of ETS exposure. IAQC discussed that the structure of peoples' homes, where they live and work, the climate, and even parental influences impact spousal assessments. SAB 1991 Review at 30. The report cited by EPA does not state workplace data should be disregarded. If at all relevant, the discussion now cited by EPA supports the opposite conclusion.

EPA also claims that workplace exposure data were
disregarded because only two studies made an attempt to classify
by amount of exposure. Again, EPA's explanation appears nowhere
in that portion of the Risk Assessment cited by the Agency.
Further, EPA's explanation appears targeted only at workplace
data contained within the spousal smoking studies and does not
address the Agency's decision to disregard workplace and
childhood exposure data reported outside spousal studies.

EPA's final proffer is that childhood studies rely upon
distant memories and more limited lifetime exposure. Again, the
record does not reveal that EPA used this as a selection
criteria. Rather, an assessment on ETS and lung cancer on which
EPA now relies states, "No consistent association has been
reported for lung cancer and exposure to ETS in childhood, which
might be expected to exert a greater effect . . . . Of course,
recall of ETS exposure in childhood is more difficult than recall
of such exposure in adulthood." E.L. Wynder & G.C. Kabat,
Environmental Tobacco Smoke and Lung Cancer: A Critical
Assessment, ORD.C.1 S59-1 (JA 5,020). Nowhere in the Assessment
is there a suggestion that childhood exposure data should be
ignored.

EPA claims it excluded the latest two U.S. spousal smoking studies because they were submitted after the close of the comment period, and EPA already had a considerable database. EPA claims the Fontham study was used because it published interim results, was the largest U.S. ETS study, and its methodology was superior to any other study. The record contains discussion of the Fontham study, even testimony by Dr. Fontham. However, the evidence is not relevant to Plaintiffs' assertion. There being no indication of study criteria, it is not possible to determine whether or why the Fontham study was "superior." Even if EPA provided criteria, comparison would not be possible since EPA provides no discussion on the two U.S. spousal studies excluded. In summary, EPA's claim of having clearly established criteria is without merit. See Bowen v. Georgetown University Hosp., 488 U.S. 204, 212, 109 S. Ct. 468, 474, 102 L. Ed. 2d 493 (1988) ("The courts may not accept appellate counsel's post hoc rationalizations for agency [orders]."); American Trucking Ass'n v. Federal Highway Admin., 51 F.3d 405, 411 (4th Cir. 1995) (If agency action is to withstand judicial review, the agency's "actual reasoning . . . must prove reasonable, not the post hoc rationalization devised during litigation.").

EPA's study selection is disturbing. First, there is evidence in the record supporting the accusation that EPA "cherry picked" its data. Without criteria for pooling studies into a meta-analysis, the court cannot determine whether the exclusion of studies likely to disprove EPA's <u>a priori</u> hypothesis was coincidence or intentional. Second, EPA's excluding nearly half of the available studies directly conflicts with EPA's purported purpose for analyzing the epidemiological studies and conflicts with EPA's Risk Assessment Guidelines. <u>See</u> ETS Risk Assessment at 4-29 ("These data should also be examined in the interest of weighing <u>all the available evidence</u>, as recommended by EPA's carcinogen risk assessment guidelines (U.S. EPA, 1986a) . . . ." (emphasis added)). Third, EPA's selective use of data conflicts with the Radon Research Act. The Act states EPA's program shall "gather data and information on <u>all aspects</u> of indoor air quality . . . ." Radon Research Act § 403(a)(1) (emphasis added). In conducting a risk assessment under the Act, EPA deliberately refused to assess information on all aspects of indoor air quality.

At the outset, the court concluded risk assessments were incidental to collecting information and making findings. EPA steps outside the court's analysis when information collection

72

becomes incidental to conducting a risk assessment. In making a
study choice, consultation with an advisory committee voicing
these concerns would have resulted, at a minimum, in a record
that explained EPA's selective use of available information.
From such record, a reviewing court could then determine whether
EPA "cherry picked" its data, and whether EPA exceeded its
statutory authority.

D.   EPA's Epidemiologic Methodology

Plaintiffs raise a list of objections asserting that
EPA deviated from accepted scientific procedure and its own Risk
Assessment Guidelines in a manner designed to ensure a
preordained outcome. Given the ETS Risk Assessment shortcomings
already discussed, it is neither necessary or desirable to delve
further into EPA's epidemiological web. However, two of
Plaintiffs' arguments require mention.[36] The first contention is

---

[36] The court finds it unnecessary to resolve Plaintiffs'
remaining methodological contentions: (1) EPA inexplicably
departed from its stated procedure for selecting risk estimates
from the spousal smoking studies when that allowed the Agency to
increase its summary risk estimate for particular studies; (2)
EPA did not include certain studies and data in its meta-analysis
in order to exclude the possibility that confounders explain the
association between ETS and cancer; (3) EPA adopted statistical
testing methods rejected by epidemiologists, ignored the

(continued...)

73

EPA switched, without explanation, from using standard 95% confidence intervals to 90% confidence intervals to enhance the likelihood that its meta-analysis would appear statistically significant. This shift assisted EPA in obtaining statistically significant results. Studies that are not statistically significant are "null studies"; they cannot support a Group A classification. See Brock v. Merrell Dow Pharm., Inc., 874 F.2d 307, 312 (5th Cir. 1989) ("If the confidence interval is so great that it includes the number 1.0, then the study will be said to show no statistically significant association between the factor and the disease.").

EPA used a 95% confidence interval in the 1990 Draft ETS Risk Assessment, but later switched to a 90% confidence interval. Most prominently, this drew criticism from IAQC's epidemiologist, who was also a contributor to the ETS Risk Assessment:

---

[36] (...continued)
possibility that more than one confounder interacting jointly could explain the claimed association, and inconsistently interpreted the results of confounding analysis to promote finding an association; (4) EPA switched from a peer-reviewed methodology to an unpublished one in excluding study bias as an explanation for the claimed association; and (5) to create critical ETS dose-response evidence, EPA inexplicably used a trend analysis that included unexposed (i.e., control) subjects, in violation of EPA's Risk Assessment Guidelines and standard epidemiologic practice.

The use of 90% confidence intervals, instead of
the conventionally used 95% confidence intervals,
is to be discouraged. It looks like a[n] attempt
to achieve statistical significance for a result
which otherwise would not achieve significance.

Geoffrey Kabat, Comments on EPA's Draft Report: "Respiratory

Health Effects of Passive Smoking: Lung Cancer and Other

Disorders", II.SAB.9.15 at 6 (July 28, 1992) (JA 12,185).

Plaintiffs argue that established epidemiologic practice is to

use 95% confidence intervals. As evidence, Plaintiffs point out

EPA's prior risk assessments, including the 1990 ETS draft,

consistently used 95% confidence intervals, as did previous ETS

analyses by IARC, NRC, and the Surgeon General.

ETS Risk Assessment Chapter 5 states:

Throughout this chapter, one-tailed tests of
significance (p=0.05) are used, which increases
the statistical ability (power) to detect an
effect. The 90% confidence intervals used for the
analyses performed are consistent with the use of
the one-tailed test. The justification for this
usage is based on the a priori hypothesis . . .
that a positive association exists between
exposure to ETS and lung cancer.

ETS Risk Assessment at 5-2. Before this court, EPA explains the

"use of the 95 percent confidence interval with the one-tailed

test . . . would have produced an apparent discrepancy: study

results that were statistically significant using the standard

p-value of .05 might nevertheless have a 95 percent confidence interval that included a relative risk of 1." (Conformed Mem. Supp. EPA's Cross Mot. Part. Summ. J. at 96.)

Plaintiffs' second methodological argument requiring comment states, EPA based ETS' Group A classification in large part on a resulting relative risk of only 1.19, without adequately explaining why the Agency had required every other Group A carcinogen to exhibit a much higher relative risk, or why it had recently found relative risks of 2.6 and 3.0 insufficient to classify other agents in Group A. All of the 15 chemicals or mixtures previously classified by EPA as Group A carcinogens have higher relative risks than ETS. See, e.g., ETS Risk Assessment at 4-15, 16 & 22 (Risk assessments on cigarette smoking demonstrate relative risks between 7 and 14.9 for lung cancer, and relative risks between 26 and 60 for undifferentiated carcinoma.); see also EPA Review Draft, Evaluation of the Potential Carcinogenicity of Electromagnetic Fields, EPA/600/6-901/005B at 6-2 (October 1990) (JA 1,562) (declining classifying EMF as carcinogenic for lack of strong association with cancer where relative risks in studies seldom exceeded 3.0). IAQC epidemiologist Dr. Kabat observed, "An association is generally considered weak if the odds ratio [relative risk] is under 3.0 and particularly when it is under 2.0, as is the case in the

76

relationship of ETS and lung cancer." E.L. Wynder & G.C. Kabat, Environmental Tobacco Smoke and Lung Cancer: A Critical Assessment, I.SAB.7.1 at 6 (JA 7,216).

EPA responds that the most impressive evidence from the epidemiologic studies is the consistent results of many studies showing increased risk, and the dose-response relationships showing the most risk to the most exposed nonsmokers. EPA explains that ETS' diluted concentration in the atmosphere accounts for the low strength of association.

The record and EPA's explanations to the court make it clear that using standard methodology, EPA could not produce statistically significant results with its selected studies. Analysis conducted with a .05 significance level and 95% confidence level included relative risks of 1. Accordingly, these results did not confirm EPA's controversial a priori hypothesis. In order to confirm its hypothesis, EPA maintained its standard significance level but lowered the confidence interval to 90%. This allowed EPA to confirm its hypothesis by finding a relative risk of 1.19, albeit a very weak association.

EPA's conduct raises several concerns besides whether a relative risk of 1.19 is credible evidence supporting a Group A classification. First, with such a weak showing, if even a fraction of Plaintiffs' allegations regarding study selection or methodology is true, EPA cannot show a statistically significant association between ETS and lung cancer.

Second, the court's conclusions regarding EPA's motive for reducing the confidence level are based upon EPA's litigation explanations and circumstantial evidence from the record. EPA does not provide explanation in the ETS Risk Assessment or administrative record. When an agency changes its methodology mid-stream, as EPA did here, it has an obligation to explain why. See Western States Petroleum Ass'n v. EPA, 87 F.3d 280, 284 (9th Cir. 1996) ("EPA `may not depart, sub silento, from its usual rules of decision to reach a different, unexplained result in a single case.'"); Natural Resources Defense Council, Inc. v. EPA, 859 F.2d 156, 205-11 (D.C. Cir. 1988) (invalidating an EPA rule because EPA failed to explain its mid-proceeding switch on the utility of an upset defense); see also Motor Vehicle Mfrs. Ass'n of U.S., Inc. v. EPA, 768 F.2d 385, 399 (D.C. Cir. 1985) (EPA failed to explain why it departed from "established specific statistical criteria for determining whether a fuel will cause a vehicle to exceed emission standards . . . .").

Finally, when an agency conducts activities under an act authorizing information collection and dissemination of findings, the agency has a duty to disseminate the findings made. EPA did not disclose in the record or in the Assessment: its inability to demonstrate a statistically significant relationship under normal methodology; the reasoning behind adopting a one-tailed test, or that only after adjusting the Agency's methodology could a weak relative risk be demonstrated. Instead of disclosing information, the Agency withheld significant portions of its findings and reasoning in striving to confirm its a priori hypothesis.

E.   **Summary of the Assessment and Record**

In reviewing the parties' arguments, the court has given the benefit of many doubts to EPA by allowing the Agency to adopt third party statements, such as IAQC reviews, as Agency reasoning. EPA, the decision maker, not IAQC, the independent advisor, has the duty to demonstrate reasoned decision making on the record. See SEC v. Chenery Corp., 332 U.S. 194, 196, 67 S. Ct. 1575, 1577, 91 L. Ed. 1995 (1947) ("[A] reviewing court, in dealing with a determination or judgment which an administrative agency alone is authorized to make, must judge the propriety of such action solely by the grounds invoked by the agency."); Motor Vehicle Mfr. Ass'n of the United States v. State Farm Mut. Auto.

Ins. Co., 463 U.S. 29, 50, 103 S. Ct. 2856, 2870, 77 L. Ed. 2d

443 (1993) ([A]n "agency's action must be upheld, if at all, on

the basis articulated by the agency itself."); see also H.R. Rep.

No. 95-722, 95th Cong., 1st Sess., 16 (1977), reprinted in 1977

U.S.C.C.A.N. 3283, 3295 (JA 652-53) (The SAB "is intended to be

advisory only. The Administrator will still have the

responsibility for making the decisions required of him by

law."). If EPA's appendages speak on behalf of the

Administrator, the opposing conclusions reached between IAQC and

the EPA Risk Criteria Office would demonstrate schizophrenia.

Even allowing EPA the benefit of now adopting IAQC reasoning, the

record does not provide answers to Plaintiffs' questions.

EPA determined it was biologically plausible that ETS causes

lung cancer. In doing so, EPA recognized problems with its

theory, namely the dissimilarities between MS and ETS. In other

areas of the Assessment, EPA relied on these dissimilarities in

justifying its methodology. EPA did not explain much of the

criteria and assertions upon which EPA's theory relies. EPA

claimed selected epidemiologic studies would affirm its

plausibility theory. The studies EPA selected did not include a

significant number of studies and data which demonstrated no

association between ETS and cancer. EPA did not explain its

criteria for study selection, thus leaving itself open to allegations of "cherry picking."

Using its normal methodology and its selected studies, EPA did not demonstrate a statistically significant association between ETS and lung cancer. This should have caused EPA to reevaluate the inference options used in establishing its plausibility theory. A risk assessment is supposed to entail the best judgment possible based upon the available evidence. See Ethyl, 541 F.2d at 24. Instead, EPA changed its methodology to find a statistically significant association. EPA claimed, but did not explain how, its theory justified changing the Agency's methodology. With the changed methodology and selected studies, EPA established evidence of a weak statistically significant association between ETS and lung cancer.

VI. MOTION TO SUPPLEMENT THE PLEADINGS

Plaintiffs have moved to supplement the pleadings pursuant to Fed. R. Civ. P. 15(d). Plaintiffs' Supplemental Pleading seeks declaratory and injunctive relief against EPA relating to the Agency's alleged unlawful efforts to regulate indoor air, tobacco products, and smoking, as documented in August 1996 by EPA's Inspector General.[37]

The Supplemental Pleading contains two counts. Supplemental Count I alleges EPA illegally funds and controls a private entity that drafts indoor air ventilation standards that are adopted in state and local building codes. Count I also alleges additional ultra vires regulatory activities by EPA in regard to indoor air and smoking through the Agency's regional offices and third parties. Supplemental Count II seeks relief from these alleged activities pursuant to the Administrative Procedure Act's bar on agency actions "in excess of statutory jurisdiction, authority, or limitations, or short of statutory right." 5 U.S.C. § 706(2)(C). Plaintiffs' proposed supplemental pleading does not affect briefing or the court's consideration of summary judgment on Counts I, II, and III. EPA responds that the proposed supplemental pleading is untimely and unrelated to the Complaint and will delay the conclusion of the case.

Fed. R. Civ. P. 15(d) allows a party with leave of court to file a supplemental pleading "setting forth transactions or

---

[37] EPA Office of Inspector General, EPA's Relationship with the American Society of Heating, Refrigerating, and Air-Conditioning Engineers (ASHRAE), Audit Report No. E1FAF5-13-0075-6100228 (August 14, 1996).

occurrences or events which have happened since the date of the pleadings sought to be supplemented." Courts apply the rule liberally to allow new claims and allegations to be added to a suit. See, e.g., Quaratino v. Tiffany & Co., 71 F.3d 58, 66 (2d Cir. 1995); Gillihan v. Shillinger, 872 F.2d 935, 941 (10th Cir. 1989); Keith v. Volpe, 858 F.2d 467, 474 (9th Cir. 1988). In reversing a district court's decision that refused leave to file a supplemental pleading, the Fourth Circuit found that supplemental pleadings so enhanced the efficient administration of justice that they should be allowed as a matter of course:

> [Supplemental pleadings are] a useful device, enabling a court to award complete relief, or more nearly complete relief, in one action, and to avoid the cost, delay and waste of separate actions which must be separately tried and prosecuted. So useful they are and of such service in the efficient administration of justice that they ought to be allowed as of course, unless some particular reason for disallowing them appears, though the court has the unquestioned right to impose terms upon their allowance when fairness appears to require them.

New Amsterdam Casualty Co. v. Waller, 323 F.2d 20, 28-29 (4th Cir. 1963). "While some relationship must exist between the newly alleged matters and the subject of the original action, they need not all arise out of the same transaction." Keith, 858 F.2d at 474. A supplemental pleading may state a new cause of action so long as the matters have some relation to the claim set forth in the original pleading. Rowe v. United States Fidelity and Guaranty Co., 421 F.2d 937, 943 (4th Cir. 1970). A court may in its discretion deny leave to file a supplemental pleading where it finds undue delay, bad faith, dilatory tactics, undue prejudice to the opposing party, or futility. Quaratino, 71 F.3d at 66.

EPA first asserts Plaintiffs' proposed supplementation is untimely because the events relevant to the new allegations occurred prior to Plaintiffs' agreeing to the joint motion to establish a briefing schedule for summary judgment. The new allegations do not, however, affect the disposition or scheduling of the court's summary judgment analysis or decision. Further, the court notes EPA's Inspector General's report was not announced or otherwise disseminated by EPA. Approximately seven months after the report was issued, Plaintiffs sought permission to file the Supplemental Pleading. Seven months is not an unreasonable amount of time for multiple plaintiffs to learn of EPA's alleged activities, investigate, develop, and agree upon a complex legal claim.

EPA next argues Plaintiffs' new allegations are not sufficiently related to the Complaint. EPA states the Complaint

84

challenges EPA's ETS Risk Assessment, whereas the proposed.

Supplemental Pleading challenges EPA's involvement with a private

entity. There are several reasons why the Complaint and proposed

Supplemental Pleading are sufficiently related. First, both

involve EPA's authority under the Radon Research Act.

Specifically, both the Complaint and Supplemental Pleading

involve EPA's authority to conduct regulatory activities under

the Act. In deciding the parties' motions for summary judgment,

the court has become familiar with the outer limits of EPA's

authority under the Radon Research Act. Second, ETS is the

object of EPA's alleged regulatory attention in each set of

allegations. As a result, EPA's conduct as alleged in the

Supplemental Pleading causes the very harm for which Plaintiffs

seek a remedy in the Complaint. Third, the court finds probable

that EPA premises its involvement with private organizations, as

alleged in the Supplemental Pleading, on the Agency's conclusions

in the ETS Risk Assessment. Fourth, the court, in resolving this

case, has become familiar with many organizations EPA has worked

with in conducting the ETS Risk Assessment and in establishing de

facto regulatory activities under the Radon Research Act.

Clearly, the Supplemental Pleading has some relation to the

Complaint.

The impact supplementing the pleadings would have in
concluding the case concerns the court. EPA has spent years
formulating and litigating the ETS Risk Assessment. Since EPA
has been aggressively coordinating with and assisting regulatory
programs based upon its ETS Risk Assessment, the court believes
EPA desires a final resolution to Plaintiffs' original claims.
EPA indicates such, stating "EPA wishes to conclude this case
challenging its ETS Risk Assessment." (Defs.' Resp. Pls.' Mot.
Supplemental Pleading at 5.) Supplementing the pleadings with
new causes of action would significantly delay final judgment
being entered in this case. As a general rule, such delay would
prevent the parties from exercising their rights to appeal.

For nearly five years, the parties have disputed the
validity of EPA's ETS Risk Assessment. Based upon the
Assessment's conclusions, EPA is involved with other government
and private entities. Resolving Plaintiffs' new allegations may
entail pretrial motions and discovery, possibly prolonging the
case for years. There is no just reason for so delaying final
judgment regarding EPA's ETS Risk Assessment. However,
Plaintiffs' new allegations are significantly related to the
Complaint. Precedent as well as principles of judicial economy
and justice urge the court to allow Plaintiffs' motion. To cure

86

this dilemma, the court will allow Plaintiffs to serve their supplemental pleading and will _sua sponte_ make an express direction for the entry of judgment regarding the parties' motions for summary judgment. Accordingly, the court's judgment will be certified for review pursuant to Fed. R. Civ. P. 54(b). Though the court creates the possibility of the parties' appealing separately under the Complaint and Supplemental Pleading, there is little risk an appellate court would be faced with redundant issues. Plaintiffs' Supplemental Pleading, although related to the issues raised in the Complaint, is factually and legally independent from the issues raised in the Complaint. EPA will have 20 days after service of the Supplemental Pleading to respond.

VII. CONCLUSION

In 1988, EPA initiated drafting policy-based recommendations about controlling ETS exposure because EPA believed ETS is a Group A carcinogen. _See, e.g._, EPA Memorandum from William K. Reilly, Administrator, to Congressman Thomas J. Bliley, Jr., U.S. House of Representatives 1 (March 24, 1992) (JA 6,374; 6,380-82) (Reilly Mem. II) (EPA began drafting a policy guide recommending workplace smoking bans before drafting the ETS Risk Assessment.)

87

Rather than reach a conclusion after collecting information, researching, and making findings, EPA categorized ETS as a "known cause of cancer" in 1989. EPA, Indoor Air Facts No. 5 Environmental Tobacco Smoke, ANR-445 (June 1989) (JA 9,409-11). EPA's Administrator admitted that EPA "managed to confuse and anger all parties to the smoking ETS debate . . . ." EPA Memorandum from William K. Reilly, Administrator, to Secretary Louis W. Sullivan 2 (July 1991) (JA 6,754). The Administrator also conceded, "[B]eginning the development of an Agency risk assessment after the commencement of work on the draft policy guide gave the appearance of . . . policy leading science . . . ." Reilly Mem. II at 1 (JA 6,391).

In conducting the Assessment, EPA deemed it biologically plausible that ETS was a carcinogen. EPA's theory was premised on the similarities between MS, SS, and ETS. In other chapters, the Agency used MS and ETS dissimilarities to justify methodology. Recognizing problems, EPA attempted to confirm the theory with epidemiologic studies. After choosing a portion of the studies, EPA did not find a statistically significant association. EPA then claimed the bioplausibility theory, renominated the a priori hypothesis, justified a more lenient methodology. With a new methodology, EPA demonstrated from the selected studies a very low relative risk for lung cancer based on ETS exposure. Based on its original theory and the weak evidence of association, EPA concluded the evidence showed a causal relationship between cancer and ETS. The administrative record contains glaring deficiencies.

The Radon Research Act authorizes information collection, research, industry inclusion, and dissemination of findings. Whether these actions authorize risk assessments is a matter of general and interstitial statutory construction. So long as information collection on all relevant aspects of indoor air quality, research, and dissemination are the lodestars, the general language of the Radon Research Act authorizes risk assessments as they are defined by NRC and explained in EPA's Risk Assessment Guidelines.

It is clear that Congress intended EPA to disseminate findings from the information researched and gathered. In this case, EPA publicly committed to a conclusion before research had begun; excluded industry by violating the Act's procedural requirements; adjusted established procedure and scientific norms to validate the Agency's public conclusion, and aggressively utilized the Act's authority to disseminate findings to establish a de facto regulatory scheme intended to restrict Plaintiffs' products and to influence public opinion.[38] In conducting.the

ETS Risk Assessment, EPA disregarded information and made

findings on selective information; did not disseminate

significant epidemiologic information; deviated from its Risk

Assessment Guidelines; failed to disclose important findings and

reasoning; and left significant questions without answers. EPA's

conduct left substantial holes in the administrative record.

While so doing, EPA produced limited evidence, then claimed the

weight of the Agency's research evidence demonstrated ETS causes

cancer.

Gathering all relevant information, researching, and

disseminating findings were subordinate to EPA's demonstrating

ETS a Group A carcinogen. EPA's conduct transgressed the general

meaning of the Radon Research Act's operative language. Further,

to the extent EPA's conduct in this matter entailed interstitial

---

[38] Given the holdings in United States v. Lopez, 514 U.S.
549, 115 S. Ct. 1624 (1995) and United States v. Hartsell, 127
F.3d 343 (4th Cir. 1997), an argument may exist concerning where
the federal government derives the authority to regulate indoor
air quality, a patently intrastate environmental concern. Being
neither interstate or commercial, it is unclear where indoor air
finds a nexus with the instrumentalities of interstate commerce
or how it substantially affects interstate commercial
transactions. The Complaint does not raise these concerns.
Since the court is granting Plaintiffs the complete relief
requested, it is unnecessary to reach these issues.

construction of the Act, the court affords no deference to EPA. Congress did not delegate rule making or regulatory authority to EPA under the Act. EPA's conduct of the ETS Risk Assessment frustrated the clear Congressional policy underlying the Radon Research Act. See 131 Cong. Rec. S7035 (May 23, 1985) (purpose of the Act is to provide clear, objective information about indoor air quality).

EPA also failed the Act's procedural requirements. In the Radon Research Act, Congress granted EPA limited research authority along with an obligation, to seek advice from a representative committee during such research. Congress intended industry representatives to be at the table and their voices heard during the research process. EPA's authority under the act is contingent upon the Agency hearing and responding to the represented constituents' concerns. The record evidence is overwhelming that IAQC was not the representative body required under the Act. Had EPA reconciled industry objections voiced from a representative body during the research process, the ETS Risk Assessment would very possibly not have been conducted in the same manner nor reached the same conclusions.

Because EPA exceeded its authority under the Radon Research Act and also failed the Act's procedural requirements, the court will direct the entry of judgment in favor of Plaintiffs' motion for summary judgment and vacate Chapters 1 thru 6 of and the Appendices to EPA's <u>Respiratory Health Effects of Passive Smoking: Lung Cancer and Other Disorders</u>, EPA/600/6-90/006F (December 1992). To ripen its judgment for purposes of appellate review pursuant to Fed. R. Civ. P. 54(b), the court will make an express determination that there is no just reason for delay. Accordingly, the court need not address Plaintiffs' remaining arguments, Counts II, III, and IV of the Complaint. The court will also grant Plaintiffs' Motion to Supplement the Pleading.

An order and judgment in accordance with this memorandum opinion will be filed contemporaneously herewith.

This the 17th day July 1998.

_____
United States District Judge

References

ACGIH (1990): American Conference of Governmental and Industrial Hygienists: *Documentation of the Threshold Limit Values and Biological Exposure Indices*. 5th Edition and supplements. ACGIH, 6500 Glenway Ave. Building D-7, Cincinnati, OH 45211-4438.

Adami H, et al. (1989): Risk of cancer in women receiving hormone replacement therapy. *Int J Cancer* 44:833-839.

Akiba S, et al. (1986): Passive Smoking and Lung Cancer Among Japanese Women. *Cancer Res*, 46:4804-4807.

Alavanja M (1993): Saturated fat intake and lung cancer risk among nonsmoking women in Missouri. *J Nat Cancer Inst* 85(23):1906-1916.

Albanes D (1989): Physical Activity and the Risk of Cancer in the NHANES I Population. *Am J Pub Health*, 79:744-750.

Albert R (1989): Carcinogen risk Assessment. *Environ Health Perspect* 81:103-105.

Altshuler B (1989): Quantitative models for lung cancer induced by cigarette smoke. *Environ Health Perspect* 81:107-108.

Agudo A, et al. (1997): Vegetable and Fruit Intake and the Risk of Lung Cancer in Women in Barcelona, Spain. *Eur J Cancer* 33:1256-1261.

Angell M (1996): *Science on trial*. W.W. Northon & Co. New York.

Angerer J (1992): Internal exposure to organic substances in a municipal waste incinerator. *Int Arch Occup Environ Health* 64:265-273.

Armitage A, et al. (1997): Environmental Tobacco Smoke: Is It Really a Carcinogen? *Med Sci Res* 25:37.

Axelsson G, et al. (1996): Dietary Factors and Lung Cancer Among Men in West Sweden. *Int J Epidemiol* 25:32-39.

Baker RR, Proctor CJ (1990): The origins and properties of environmental tobacco smoke. *Envir Intern* 16:231-245.

Benowitz NL, et al. (1991): Stable isotope studies of nicotine kinetics and bioavailability. *Clin Pharmacol Ther* 49:270-277

Blair A, et al. (1995): "Guidelines for Application of MetaAnalysis in Environmental Epidemiology," *Regul Toxicol Pharmacol* 22:189-197.

Boffetta P, et al. (1998): Multicenter casecontrol study of exposure to environmental tobacco smoke and lung cancer in Europe. *J Nat Cancer Inst* 90:1440-1450.

Brandt AM (1998): Blow some my way: passive smoking, risk and American culture. In: *Ashes to ashes: the history of smoking and health*. Lock S, et al., Eds., pp. 164-187. Radopi B.V., Amsterdam & Atlanta.

Breslow N, Day N (1980): *Statistical Methods in Cancer Research: Volume 1 The Analysis of Case-Control Studies*, International Agency for Research on Cancer, Scientific Publications, No. 32, Lyon, France.

Breslow N, Day N (1987): *Statistical Methods in Cancer Research: Volume 2 The Design and Analysis of Cohort Studies*. International Agency for Research on Cancer, Scientific Publications, No. 82, Lyon, France.

Bretthauer EW (1992): Assistant Administrator for Research and Development, EPA. Letter to JJ Tozzi. December 17, 1992, Washington DC.

Brown S, et al. (1995): The Association of Economic Status With the Occurrence of Lung Cancer. *Cancer* 36:1903-1911.

Brownson R, et al. (1987): Risk Factors for Adenocarcinoma of the Lung. *Am J Epidemiol* 125:25-34.

Brownson RC, et al. (1992): Passive smoking and lung cancer in non-smoking women. *Am J Publ Health* 82:1525-1530.

Brownson RC, et al. (1993): Reliability of passive smoke exposure histories in a case control study of lung cancer. *Intern J Epidemiol* 22:804-808

Brownson R, et al. (1997): Family History of Cancer and Risk of Lung Cancer in Lifetime Non-Smokers and Long-Term Ex-Smokers. *Int J Epidemiol* 26(2):256-263.

Brugnone F, et al. (1992): Reference values for blood benzene in the occupationally unexposed general population. *Int Arch Occup Environ Health* 64:179-184.

Buffler P, et al. (1984): The Causes of Lung Cancer in Texas. In: *Lung Cancer: Causes and Prevention* (Mizzell M, Correa P, Eds.):, pp. 83-99. Verlag Chemie International New York.

Butler T (1988): *The Relationship of Passive Smoking to Various Health Outcomes Among SeventhDay Adventists in California*. Ph.D. Dissertation, University of California, Los Angeles, California.

Byers T, et al. (1987): Diet and Lung Cancer Risk: Findings from the Western New York Diet Study. *Am J Epidemiol* 125:351-363.

Candelora E, et al. (1992): Dietary Intake and Risk of Lung Cancer in Women Who Never Smoked. *Nutr Cancer* 17(3):263-270.

Cardenas V, et al. (1997): Environmental Tobacco Smoke and Lung Cancer Mortality in the American Cancer Society's Cancer Prevention Study II. *Cancer Causes Control* 8:57-64.

CEPA (1997): *Health effects of exposure to environmental tobacco smoke. Final Report*. California Environmental protection Agency. Office of Environmental Hazards Assessment. Sacramento, California.

Chan W, Fung S (1982): Lung Cancer in Non-Smokers in Hong Kong. In: *Cancer Campaign, Volume 6, Cancer Epidemiology* (Grundmann E, Ed.):, pp. 199-202, Gustav Fischer Verlag, Stuttgart, Germany.

Chen C (1990): Epidemiologic Characteristics and Multiple Risk Factors of Lung Cancer in Taiwan. *Anticancer Res* 10:971-976.

Chen T (1989): A Review of Methods for Misclassified Categorical Data in Epidemiology. *Statistics in Med*, 8:1095-1106.

Choi SY, et al. (1989): A Case-Control Study on Risk Factors in Lung Cancer. *Korean J Epidemiol* 11:66-80.

Collier AM, et al. (1992): Cotinine elimination in young children as a function of age, sex, and race following ETS exposure (Abstract). *Am Rev Respir Dis* 145(4pt2):532A.

Correa P, et al. (1983): Passive Smoking and Lung Cancer. *Lancet* 2:595-597.

Coultas DB, et al. (1990a): Variability of measures of exposure to environmental tobacco smoke in the home. *Am Rev Respir Dis* 142: 602-606.

Coultas DB, et al. (1990b): A personal monitoring study to assess the workplace exposure to environmental tobacco smoke. *Am J Publ Health* 80:988-990.

Cress RD, et al. (1994): Characteristics of women nonsmokers exposed to passive smoke. *Prev Med* 23:40-47.

Crouse W (1988): *Results from a survey of environmental tobacco smoke in restaurants*. Presented at the APCA International Conference, Niagara Falls, NY.

Dai XD, et al. (1996): The Etiology of Lung Cancer in Nonsmoking Females in Harbin, China. *Lung Cancer* 14(Suppl.1):S85-91.

Daling JR, et al. (1994): Risk of breast cancer among young women: relationship to induced abortion. *J Natl Cancer Inst* 86:1584-92.

Delfino RJ, et al. (1993): Questionnaire assessment of recent exposure to environmental tobacco smoke in relation to salivary cotinine. *Eur Respir J* 6:1104-1108.

Dement J, et al. (1994): FollowUp Study of Chrisotyle Asbestos Textile Workers: Cohort Mortality and CaseControl Analyses. *Am J Ind Med* 26:431-447.

De Stefani E, et al. (1997): Fatty Foods and the Risk of Lung Cancer: A Case-Control Study From Uruguay. *Int J Cancer* 71:760-766.

Dickersin K (1997): How important is publication bias? A synthesis of available data. *AIDS Educ Prev* 9:15-21.

Doll R, Peto R (1976): Mortality in relation to smoking: 20 years' observations on male British doctors. *Br Med J* 2:1525-1536.

Doll R, Peto R (1978): Cigarette smoking and bronchial carcinoma: dose and time relationships among regular smokers and lifelong non-smokers. *J Epidemiol Commun Health* 32:303-313.

Doll R (1978): An epidemiologic perspective of the biology of cancer. *Cancer Res* 38:3573-3583.

Doll R, et al. (1980): Mortality in relation to smoking: 22 years' observations on female British doctors. *Br Med J* 280:967-971.

Doll R, et al. (1994): Mortality in relation to smoking: 40 years' observations in male British doctors. *Br Med J* 309:901-911.

Domino EF, et al. (1993): The relevance of nicotine content of common vegetables to the identification of passive tobacco smokers. *Med Sci Res* 21:571-572.

Easterbrook P, et al. (1991): Publication bias in clinical research. *Lancet* 337:867-872.

Edlin C, et al. (1984): Radon in Homes: A Possible Cause of Lung Cancer. *Scand J Work Environ Health* 10:25-34.

Emmons KM, et al. (1992): Exposure to environmental tobacco smoke in naturalistic settings. *Am J Publ Health* 82:24-28

Emmons K, et al. (1995): Dietary intake and exposure to environmental tobacco smoke in a worksite population. *Eu J Clin Nutr* 49:336-343.

Fontham ET, et al. (1991): Lung cancer in nonsmoking women: A multicenter casecontrol study. *Cancer Epidemiol Biomarkers Prev* 1: 35-43.

Fontham E, et al. (1992): Lung Cancer in Nonsmoking Women: Dietary Antioxidants. *Cancer Epidemiol Biomarkers Prev* 1:249.

Fontham E, et al. (1994): Environmental Tobacco Smoke and Lung Cancer in Nonsmoking Women: A Multicenter Study. *J Am Med Assn* 271:1752-1759.

Freund KM, et al. (1993): The health risks of smoking. The Framingham study: 34 years of followup. *Ann Epidemiol* 3:417-424.

Gao Y, et al. (1987): Lung Cancer Among Chinese Women. *Int J Cancer* 40:604-609.

Gaylor DW, et al. (1997): Health Risk assessment practices in the U.S. Food and Drug Administration. *Regulatory Toxicology and Pharmacology* 26:307-321, 1997.

Garfinkel L (1981): Time Trends in Lung Cancer Mortality Among Nonsmokers. *J Nat Cancer Inst* 66:1061-1066.

Garfinkel L, et al. (1985): Involuntary Smoking and Lung Cancer: A CaseControl Study. *J Nat Cancer Inst* 75:463-469.

Geng G, et al. (1988): On the Relationship Between Smoking and Female Lung Cancer. In: *Smoking and Health 1987* (Aoki M, et al., Eds.):, pp. 483-86, Elsevier Science Publishers, Amsterdam.

Givens G, et al. (1997): Publication Bias in MetaAnalysis: A Bayesian Data Augmentation Approach To Account For Issues Exemplified in the Passive Smoking Debate. *Stat Sci* 12:221-250.

Goodman M, et al. (1988): The Effect of Dietary Cholesterol and Fat on the Risk of Lung Cancer in Hawaii. *Am J Epidemiol* 128:1241-1255.

Gori GB (1976): Low risk cigarettes: a prescription. *Science* 194:1243-1246.

Gori GB, Mantel N (1991): Mainstream and environmental tobacco smoke. *Regul Toxicol Pharmacol* 14:88-105.

Gori GB (1998a): Epidemiology and public health: is a new paradigm needed or a new ethic? *J Clin Epidemiol* 51:637-641.

Gori GB (1998b): Reply to the preceding dissent. *J Clin Epidemiol* 51: 647-649.

Gravelle JG, Zimmermann D (1994): *Cigarette taxes to fund health care reform: An economic analysis.* Congressional Research Services, The Library of Congress, Washington, DC.

Greenwald AG (1975): Consequences of prejudices against the null hypothesis. *Psychol. Bull* 82:1-20.

Guerin MR, et al. (1987): Measuring environmental emissions from tobacco combustion: sidestream cigarette smoke literature review. *Atmos Environ* 21:291-297.

Gustavsson P, et al. (1990): Lung Cancer and Exposure to Diesel Exhaust Among Bus Garage Workers. *Scand J Work Environ Health* 16:334-54.

Hackshaw A, et al. (1997): The Accumulated Evidence on Lung Cancer and Environmental Tobacco Smoke. *Br Med J* 315:980-988.

Haevner DL, et al. (1996): Determination of volatile organic compounds and respirable suspended particulate matter in New Jersey and Pennsylvania homes and workplaces. *Environ Int* 22:159-183.

Hatziandreu EJ, et al (1989): The reliability of self-reported cigarette consumption in the United States. *Am J Publ Health* 79:1020-1023.

Hayes R, et al.(1989): Lung Cancer in Motor Exhaust-Related Occupations. *Am J Ind Med* 16:685-695.

Hill AB (1965): The environment and disease: Association or Causation? *Proc R Soc Med,* 58:295-300.

Hinds M, et al. (1982): Tuberculosis and Lung Cancer Risk in Non-Smoking Women. *Am Rev Respir Dis* 125:776-778.

Hirayama T (1981): Non-Smoking Wives of Heavy Smokers a Higher Risk of Lung Cancer: A Study From Japan. *Br Med J* 282:183-185.

Hirayama T (1984): Lung cancer in Japan: effects of nutrition on passive smoking. In: *Lung cancer: causes and prevention.* Mizell M, Correa P, Eds. pp.175-195. Verlag Chemie International Inc., New York.

Hoffmann D, Hecht SS (1989): Advances in tobacco carcinogenesis. In: *Chemical carcinogenesis and mutagenesis.* Cooper CS, Grover PL, eds., Springer-Verlag, New York.

Hole D, et al. (1989): Passive Smoking and Cardiorespiratory Health in a General Population in the West of Scotland. *Br Med J* 299:423-427.

Horwitz R, et al. (1988): An Ecogenetic Hypothesis for Lung Cancer in Women. *Arch Intern Med* 148:2609-2612.

Humble C, et al. (1987): Marriage to a Smoker and Lung Cancer Risk. *Am J Pub Health* 77:598-602.

IARC (1986): *Tobacco smoking: Monographs on the Evaluation of the Carcinogenic Risk of Chemicals to Humans*, Vol 38. International Agency for Research on Cancer, World Health Organization, Lyon, France.

ICSH (1998): *Fourth report of the Independent Committee on Smoking and Health.* Her Majesty's Stationery Office, London.

Inoue R, Hirayama T (1988): Passive Smoking and Lung Cancer in Women. In: *Smoking and Health 1987.* Aoki M, et al., Eds. pp. 283-285. Elsevier Science Publishers, Amsterdam.

Jacobsson R, et al. (1997): Increased Risk of Lung Cancer Among Professional Drivers in Urban But Not Rural Areas of Sweden. *Occup Environ Med* 54:189-193.

Jain M, et al. (1990): Dietary Factors and Risk of Lung Cancer: Results from a CaseControl Study, Toronto, 1981-85. *Int J Cancer* 45:287293.

Janerich D, et al. (1990): Lung Cancer and Exposure to Tobacco Smoke in the Household. *N Engl J Med* 323:632-636.

Jarvis MJ, et al. (1987): Comparison of tests used to distinguish smokers from nonsmokers. *Am J Publ Health*, 77:1435-1438.

Jenkins RA, et al. (1996): Exposure to environmental tobacco smoke in sixteen cities in the United States as determined by personal breathing zone air sampling. *J Exp Anal Environ Epidemiol* 6:473-502.

Jöckel K-H (1991): *Passive Smoking*—Evaluation of the Epidemiological Findings. Presentation to the Association of German Engineers, Mannheim Colloquium, VDI Reports 888.

Jöckel K-H (1997): *Environmental Tobacco Smoke and Lung Cancer in Germany.* Position paper on Public Hearing of Experts on the Law on Protection of NonSmokers, Health Policy Questions/Child and Youth Protection, Bonn, Germany.

Jöckel K-H (1998) Environmental tobacco smoke and lung cancer. *Epidemiology* 9:672-675.

Kabat G, Wynder E (1984): Lung Cancer in Nonsmokers. *Cancer* 53:1214-1221.

Kabat G (1990): Epidemiological Studies of the Relationship Between Passive Smoking and Lung Cancer. In: *Toxicology Forum: 1990 Annual Winter Meeting.* pp.187-189. Washington, DC.

Kabat G (1994): Aspects of the Epidemiology of Lung Cancer in Smokers and Nonsmokers in the United States. In: *Proceedings of the International Symposium on Lifestyle Factors and Human Lung Cancer,* Guangzhou, China.

Kabat GC, et al. (1995): Relation between exposure to environmental tobacco smoke and lung cancer in lifetime nonsmokers. *Am J Epidemiol* 142:141-148

Kalandidi A, et al. (1990): Passive Smoking and Diet in the Etiology of Lung Cancer Among Nonsmokers. *Cancer Causes Control* 1:15-21.

Klawansky S, Fox MS (1984): A growth rate distribution model for the age dependence of human cancer incidence: A proposed role for promotion in cancer of the lung and breast. *J Theor Biol* 111:531-587.

Klesges LM, et al. (1992): Discrepancies between self-reported smoking and carboxyhemoglobin An analysis of the Second National Health and Nutrition Survey. *Am J Publ Health* 82:1026-1029.

Kluger R (1996): *Ashes to Ashes: American's hundred-year cigarette war, the public health, and the unabashed triumph of Philip Morris.* A. Knopf, New York.

Ko YC, et al. (1997): Risk Factors for Primary Lung Cancer Among Non-Smoking Women in Taiwan. *Int J Epidemiol* 26:24-31.

Koo L, et al. (1987a): Measurements of Passive Smoking and Estimates of Lung Cancer Risk Among Non-Smoking Chinese Females. *Int J Cancer* 39:162-169.

Koo L, et al. (1997b): Dietary and Lifestyle Correlates of Passive Smoking in Hong Kong, Japan, Sweden and the USA. *Soc Sci Med* 45:159-169.

Koo L, (1988): Dietary Habits and Lung Cancer Risk Among Chinese Females in Hong Kong Who Never Smoked. *Nutr Cancer* 11:155-172.

Knekt P, et al.(1996): Elevated Lung Cancer Risk Among Persons With Depressed Mood. *Am J Epidemiol*, 144:1096-1103.

Kulessa C, et al. (1989): Psychosocial Personality Traits and Cigarette Smoking Among Bronchial Carcinoma Patients. *Stress Med* 5:37-46.

Kvale G, et al. (1986): Occupational Exposure and Lung Cancer Risk. *Int J Cancer* 37:185-193.

Lalonde M (1974): *A new perspective on the health of Canadians.* Health and Welfare Canada. Ottawa. Canada.

Lam W (1985): *A Clinical and Epidemiological Study of Carcinoma of Lung in Hong Kong.* M.D. Dissertation, Hong Kong University, Hong Kong.

Lam T, et al. (1987): Smoking, Passive Smoking and Histological Types in Lung Cancer in Hong Kong Chinese Women. *Br J Cancer* 6: 673-678.

Lange P, et al. (1990): Ventilatory Function and Chronic Mucus Hypersecretion as Predictors of Death from Lung Cancer. *Am Rev Respir Dis* 141:613-617.

Last J (1994): New pathways in an age of ecological and ethical concerns. *Int J Epidemiol* 23:1-4.

Lee PN, et al. (1986): Relationship of Passive Smoking to Risk of Lung Cancer and Other Smoking-Associated Diseases. *Br J Cancer* 54: 97-105.

Lee PN (1992): *Environmental Tobacco Smoke and Mortality.* Karger, Basel, Switzerland.

Lee PN (1993a): An estimate of adult mortality in the United States from passive smoking. *Envir Intern* 19:91-100.

Lee PN (1993b): An Assessment of the Epidemiological Evidence Relating Lung Cancer Risk in Never Smokers to Environmental Tobacco Smoke Exposure. In: *Environmental Tobacco Smoke* (Kasuga H, ed.): pp.28-70. Springer-Verlag, New York.

Lee PN, Forey B (1995): Misclassification of Smoking Habits as Determined by Cotinine or by Repeated Self-Report—A Summary From 42 Studies. *J Smoking-Related Dis* 6:109-129.

Lee PN, Forey B (1996): Misclassification of Smoking Habits as a Source of Bias in the Study of Environmental Tobacco Smoke and Lung Cancer. *Statistics Med*, 15:581-605.

Lee PN (1998): Difficulties in assessing the relationship between passive smoking and lung cancer. *Stat Met Med Res*, 7:137-163.

Lee I, Paffenbarger R (1994): Physical Activity and Its Relation to Cancer Risk. *Med Sci Sport Exerc* 26:831-837.

Lees R, et al. (1987): A Case-Control Study of Lung Cancer Relative to Domestic Radon Exposure. *Int J Epidemiol* 16:7-12.

Lei YX, et al. (1996): Some Lifestyle Factors in Human Lung Cancer: A Case-Control Study of 792 Lung Cancer Cases. *Lung Cancer* 14(Suppl.1):S121-S136.

Le Marchand L, et al. (1989): Vegetable consumption and lung cancer risk: a population-based case-control study in Hawaii. *JNCI* 81:1158-1164.

Le Marchand L, et al. (1991): Dietary patterns of female nonsmokers with and without exposure to environmental tobacco smoke. *Cancer Cause Contr* 2:11-16.

LeVois ME, Layard MW (1994): Inconsistencies between workplace and spousal studies of environmental tobacco smoke and lung cancer. *Regul Toxicol Pharmacol* 19:309-316.

LeVois M, Switzer P (1998): Differential Exposure Misclassification in Case-Control Studies of Environmental Tobacco Smoke and Lung Cancer. *J Clin Epidemiol* 51:37-54.

Liu Q, et al. (1993): Indoor Air Pollution and Lung Cancer in Guangzhou, People's Republic of China. *Am J Epidemiol* 137:145-154.

Liu Z, et al. (1991): Smoking and Other Risk Factors for Lung Cancer in Xuanwei, China. *Int J Epidemiol* 20:25-31.

Luik JC (1996): *Smokescreen: passive smoking and public policy.* Institute of Public Affairs, Melbourne.

Luo RX, et al. (1996): Indoor Burning Coal Air Pollution and Lung Cancer: A Case-Control Study in Fuzhou, China. *Lung Cancer* 14(Suppl.1):S113-119.

Mantel N, Haenszel W (1959): Statistical Aspects of the Analysis of Data From Retrospective Studies of Disease. *J Nat Cancer Inst* 22:719-748.

Margetts BM, Jackson AA (1993): Interactions between people's diet and their smoking habits: the dietary and nutritional survey of British adults. *Br Med J* 307:1381-1384.

Matanoski G, et al. (1995): Characteristics of Nonsmoking Women in NHANES I and NHANES II Epidemiologic Follow-Up Study With Exposure to Spouses Who Smoke. *Am J Epidemiol* 142:149-157.

Mercer RR, Crapo JD (1993): Three-dimensional analysis of lung structure and its application to pulmonary dosimetry models. In: *Toxicology of the lung*, Gardner DE, et al., eds. Raven Press, New York.

Mettlin C, (1989): Milk Drinking, Other Beverage Habits, and Lung Cancer Risk. *Int J Cancer* 43:608-612.

Miesner EA, et al. (1989): Particulate and nicotine sampling in public facilities and offices. *J Air Pollut Control Assoc*, 39:1577-1582.

Mumford J, et al. (1987): Lung Cancer and Indoor Air Pollution in Xuan Wei, China. *Science* 235:217-220.

NAS, (1986): National Research Council, National Academy of Sciences. *Environmental Tobacco Smoke: measuring exposures and assessing health effects*. National Academy Press, Washington, DC

NAS (1992): *Responsible Science: Ensuring the integrity of the research process*, Volume I. National Academy of Sciences, National Academy Press, Washington, DC.

National Cancer Institute (1994): *Abortion and possible risk for breast cancer: analysis and inconsistencies*. Press Release October 26, 1994.

Nelson PR, et al. (1997): Composition of environmental tobacco smoke (ETS) from international cigarettes and determination of ETS-RSP:particulate marker ratios. *Environ Int* 23:47-52.

NTP (1998): *Report on Carcinogens Subcommittee. Board of Scientific Counselors*. National Toxicology Program. Session of December 2-3, 1998. National Institute of Environmental Health Sciences, Research Triangle Park, North Carolina.

Nyberg F, et al. (1997): Environmental Tobacco Smoke and Lung Cancer —Does Time Since Exposure Play a Role? *Epidemiology* 8:S38.

Ogden MW, et al. (1997): National incidence of smoking and misclassification among U.S. married female population. *J Clin Epidemiol* 50:253-263.

Ohlin P, et al. (1976): Carbon monoxide blood levels and reported cessation of smoking. *Psychopharmacology* (Berlin) 49:263-265.

Oksa P, et al. (1997): Cancer Incidence and mortality among Finnish asbestos sprayers and in asbestosis and silicosis patients. *Am J Ind Med* 31:693-698.

Oldaker GB, et al. (1990): Results from surveys of environmental tobacco smoke in offices and restaurants. In: *Indoor air quality*. Kasuga H, ed., pp.99-104. Springer Verlag, Berlin.

Ooi W, et al. (1986): Increased Familial Risk for Lung Cancer. *J Nat Cancer Inst* 76:217-222.

Osteen WL (1998): Order and Judgment in: *Flue-cured Tobacco Cooperative Stabilization Corporation et al. V. United States Environmental Protection Agency and Carol Browner, Administrator, Environmental Protection Agency.* U.S. District Court, Middle District of North Carolina, Winston-Salem Division. July, 17.

Pastorino U, et al. (1987): Vitamin A and female lung cancer: A case-control study on plasma and diet. *Nutr Cancer* 10:171-179.

Perbellini L, et al. (1988): Environmental and occupational exposure to benzene by analysis of breath and blood. *Br J Ind Med* 45:345-352.

Perez-Stable E, et al. (1992): Misclassification of smoking status by self-reported cigarette consumption. *Am Rev Respir Dis* 145:53-57.

Pershagen G, et al. (1987): Passive Smoking and Lung Cancer in Swedish Women. *Am J Epidemiol* 125:17-24.

Phillips K, et al (1994): Assessment of personal exposures to environmental tobacco smoke in British nonsmokers. *Environ Int* 20:693-712.

Phillips K, et al. (1996): Assessment of air quality in Stockholm by personal monitoring of nonsmokers for respirable suspended particles and environmental tobacco smoke. *Scand J Work Environ Health* 22(1):1-24.

Phillips K, et al (1997a): Assessment of air quality in Barcelona by personal monitoring of nonsmokers for respirable suspended particles and environmental tobacco smoke. *Environ Int* 23:173-196.

Phillips K, et al (1997b): Assessment of air quality in Turin by personal monitoring of nonsmokers for respirable suspended particles and environmental tobacco smoke. *Environ Int* 23:851-871.

Phillips K, et al. (1998): Assessment of environmental tobacco smoke and respirable suspended particle exposures for nonsmokers in Prague using personal monitoring. *Int Arch Occup Environ Health* 71:379-390.

Pollack E. et al. (1984): Prospective Study of Alcohol Consumption and Cancer. *N Engl J Med* 310:617-621.

Potter J, et al. (1992): Alcohol, Beer and Lung Cancer in Post-menopausal Women: The Iowa Women Health Study. *Ann Epidemiol* 2:587-595.

Proctor CJ, et al. (1989): Measurement of environmental tobacco smoke in an air-conditioned office building. In: *Present and future of indoor air quality.* Bieva CJ, et al., eds., pp.169-172. Elsevier, Amsterdam.

Proctor CJ (1990): Measurement of ETS on smoking allowed and smoking prohibited public buses. In: *Indoor air quality and ventilation.* Luna F, Reynolds GL, eds., pp.427-436. Selper, London.

Radon Research Act (1986): *Radon Gas and Indoor Air Quality Research Act of 1986.* Pub. L. No. 99-499, 100 Stat.1758-60. Codified 1994 at U.S.C. 5-7401 note.

Raffin E, et al. (1993): Incidence of Lung Cancer by Histological Type Among Asbestos Cement Workers in Denmark. *Br J Ind Med,* 50: 85-89.

Reilly WE (1991): *Memorandum from William E. Reilly, Administrator, US Environmental Protection Agency, to Louis W. Sullivan, Secretary, US Department of Health and Human Services,* July 2, 1991. US Environmental Protection Agency. Washington DC.

Redhead C, Rowberg R (1995): *Environmental Tobacco Smoke and Lung Cancer Risk,* US Congressional Research Service, US Library of Congress, Washington, DC.

Rodgman A (1992): Environmental tobacco smoke. *Regul Toxicol Pharmacol* 16:223-224.

Rosenberg WG (1991): Assistant EPA Administrator for Air and Radiation. *Letter to Erich Bretthauer, Assistant EPA Administrator for Research and Development, October 7, 1991. Letter to Donald G. Barnes, Director, EPA Science Advisory Board, June 28, 1991.*

Rosenberg L (1994): Induced abortion and breast cancer: More scientific data are needed. *J Nat Cancer Inst* 86:1569-1570.

Rothman KJ (1982): Causation and causal inference. In: *Cancer epidemiology and prevention.* Schottenfeld D, Fraumeni JF, eds. pp. 15-22. WB Saunders Co., Philadelphia.

Rothman KJ (1986): *Modern Epidemiology.* Little, Brown & Co, Boston.

Rylander R, (1996): Lung Cancer, Smoking, and Diet Among Swedish Men. *Lung Cancer* 14(Supp.1):S75-83.

Sakurai R, et al. (1989): Prognosis of Female Patients With Pulmonary Tuberculosis. *Japan J Med* 28:471-477.

Samet J, et al. (1986): Personal and Family History of Respiratory Disease and Lung Cancer Risk. *Am Rev Respir Dis* 134:466-470.

Samet JM (1992): Environmental tobacco smoke. In: *Environmental toxicants.* Lippmann M, ed. Van Nostrand & Reinhold, New York.

Sankaranarayanan R, et al. (1994): A Case-Control Study of Diet and Lung Cancer in Kerala, South India. *Int J Med* 58:644-649.

Saracci R (1995): Ethical Issues in Assessing Scientific Evidence. *Medicina del Lavoro* 86:174-177.

Schwartz A, et al. (1996): Familial risk of lung cancer among nonsmokers and their Relatives. *Am J Epidemiol* 144:554-562.

SCOTH (1998): *Report of the Scientific Committee on Tobacco and Health.* Department of Health. Department of Health and Social Services, Northern Ireland. The Scottish Office Department of Health. Welsh Office. The Stationery Office. London.

Severson R, et al. (1989): A Prospective Analysis of Physical Activity and Cancer. *Am J Epidemiol* 130:522-529.

Shapiro S (1997): Is MetaAnalysis a Valid Approach to the Evaluation of Small Effects in Observational Studies? *J Clin Epidemiol* 50: 223-229.

Schaffner KF (1991): Causing harm: Epidemiological and physiological concepts of causation. In: *Acceptable evidence: Science and values in risk management*. Mayo DG, Hollander RD, eds. Oxford University Press, New York.

Shapiro S (1998): Is metaanalysis a valid approach to the evaluation of small effects? In: *Epidemiological practices in research on small effects*. Hoffmann H, Szklo M, Thamm M, eds. Springer Verlag, Berlin.

Sheldon LS, et al. (1989): *An investigation of infiltration and indoor air quality*. Final report to the New York State Energy Research and Development Authority. Albany, New York.

Shen XB, et al. (1996): Relationship of Passive Smoking and Pulmonary Adenocarcinoma in Non-Smoking Women—A Case Control Study in Nanjing, P.R. China. *Epidemiology* 7:S20.

Shimizu H, et al. (1998): A Case Control Study of Lung Cancer in Nonsmoking Women. *Tohoku J Exper Med* 154:389-397.

Shy C, (1984): Air Pollution and Lung Cancer. In: *Lung Cancer: Causes and Prevention* (Mizell M, Correa P, eds.), pp. 65-72. Verlag Chemie International, Berlin.

Sidney S, et al. (1989): Dietary intake of carotene in nonsmokers with and without passive smoking at home. *Am J Epidemiol* 129:1305-1309.

Sillett RW, et al. (1978): Deception among smokers. *Br Med J* 2:1185-1186.

Sobue T, et al. (1990): Association of Indoor Air Pollution and Passive Smoking With Lung Cancer in Osaka, Japan. *Japan J Cancer Clin* 36:329-333.

Spengler JD, et al. (1981): Long-term measurement of respirable sulphates and particles inside and outside homes. *Atmos Environ* 15:23-30.

Spengler JD, et al. (1985): Personal exposure to respirable particulates and implications for air pollution epidemiology. *Environ Sci Technol* 19:700-707.

Steenland K (1992): Passive smoking and the risk of heart disease. *JAMA* 267:94-99.

Sterling TD, Sterling EM (1983): Investigations on the effect of regulating smoking on levels of indoor pollution and on the perception of health and comfort of office workers. *Eu J Respir Dis* 65:(Supp. 133):17-32.

Sterling EM, et al. (1996): Assessment of nonsmoker exposure to environmental tobacco smoke using personal-exposure and fixed-location monitoring. *Indoor Build Environ* 5:112-125.

Stockwell HG, et al. (1992): Environmental tobacco smoke and lung cancer risk in nonsmoking women. *JNCI* 84:1417-1422.

Stookey GK, et al. (1987): Evaluation of biochemical validation measures in determination of smoking status. *J Dent Res* 66:1597-1601.

Stolwijk JAJ (1993): Statement: Transcript of the July 15, 1993 ETS session, Toxicology Forum, Aspen, Colorado. Toxicology Forum, Washington DC.

Sullum J (1998): *For your own good*, The Free Press, New York.

Sun X, et al. (1996): Environmental Tobacco Smoke (ETS): and Lung Cancer Among Nonsmoking Women in Harbin, China. *Lung Cancer* 14(Suppl.1):S237.

Svensson C, et al. (1989): Smoking and Passive Smoking in Relation to Lung Cancer in Women. *Acta Oncologica* 28:623-629.

Teel RW, Castonguay A (1992): Antimutagenic effects of polyphenolic compounds. *Cancer Lett* 66:107-113.

Teich AH, Frankel MS (1992): *Good science and responsible scientists. Meeting the challenge of fraud and misconduct in science.* American Association for the Advancement of Science, Washington, DC.

Tenkanen L, et al. (1987): Smoking and Cardiac Symptoms as Predictors of Lung Cancer. *J Chronic Dis* 40:1121-1128.

Thornton A, et al. (1994): Differences between smokers, exsmokers, passive smokers, and nonsmokers. *J Clin Epidemiol* 47:1143-1162.

Thune I, Lund E (1997): The Influence of Physical Activity on Lung Cancer Risk: A Prospective Study of 81,516 Men and Women. *Int J Cancer* 70:57-62.

Trichopoulos D, et al. (1981): Lung Cancer and Passive Smoking. *Int J Cancer* 27:1-4.

Trichopoulos D, et al. (1983): Lung Cancer and Passive Smoking: Conclusion of Greek Study. *Lancet* 2:677-678.

Tsuda T, et al. (1995): Ingested Arsenic and Internal Cancer: A Historical Cohort Followed for 33 Years. *Am J Epidemiol* 141:198-209.

van Loon A, et al. (1997): Socioeconomic Status and Lung Cancer Incidence in Men in the Netherlands: Is There a Role for Occupational Exposure? *J Epidemiol Commun. Health* 51:24-29.

USEPA (1986): U.S. Environmental Protection Agency. *Guidelines for carcinogen risk assessment.* Fed Reg 51:185:33993-34003; September 24

USEPA (1989): *Indoor air facts No.5. Environmental tobacco smoke.* US Environmental Protection Agency. Office of Air and Radiation. ANR-445. June 1989. Washington DC.

USEPA (1990a): United States Environmental Protection Agency. *Health Effects of Passive Smoking: Assessment of lung cancer in adults and respiratory disorders in children.* Office of Research and Development, Washington, DC.

USEPA (1990b): U.S. Environmental Protection Agency. *Technical Support Document for the 1990 Citizens Guide to Radon.* USEPA. Office of Radiation Programs, Radon Division. August 16, 1990, Washington, DC.

USEPA (1992a): U.S. Environmental Protection Agency. Science Advisory Board, *Environmental Tobacco Smoke Review Panel.* July 21-22, 1992. Crystal City Holiday Inn, Arlington, VA 22202. Transcript from: Barrera Associates Inc., 733 15th Street NW, Suite 1120, Washington, DC.

USEPA (1992b): United States Environmental Protection Agency. *Respiratory health effects of passive smoking: Lung Cancer and other Disorders.* May 1992. Office of Research and Development, Washington DC.

USEPA (1992c): United States Environmental Protection Agency. *Respiratory health effects of passive smoking. Lung cancer and other disorders.* December 1992. Office of Research and Development, Washington, DC.

USEPA (1992d): United States Environmental Protection Agency. *Reviews of the EPA-ETS report by the EPA Environmental Assessment Office, Cincinnati, OH*: Memorandum of April 27, 1990 from Chris DeRosa to William Farland. Memorandum of March 24, 1992 from Terry Harvey to Linda Bailey-Becht. US Environmental Protection Agency, Washington, DC.

USEPA (1992e): United States Environmental Protection Agency. *Safeguarding the future: credible science, credible decisions. The report of an expert panel on the role of science at EPA.* EPA/600/9-91/050. March 1992. Office of the Administrator. Washington, DC.

USEPA (1994): *Setting the record straight: Second hand smoke is a preventable health risk.* EPA Publication 402-F-94-005. Environmental Protection Agency, Washington, DC.

USEPA (1996): *Proposed guidelines for carcinogen risk assessment;* Notice. Fed Reg 61, No.79:17960-18011

USEPA (1998): *Flue-Cured Tobacco Cooperative Stabilization Corp., et al. v. U.S. Environmental Protection Agency,* 875 F. Supp. 1137 (M.D.N.C. 1944), *appeals pending,* Nos. 98-2407 & 98-2473 (4th Cir.).

USOSHA (1994): US Occupational Safety and Health Administration. *Indoor air quality;* Proposed Rule. Fed Reg 59(65):, April 5, 1994:15969-16039.

USSG (1964): *Smoking and health. Report of the advisory committee to the Surgeon General of the Public Health Service.* U.S. Department of Health, Education, and Welfare. Public Health Service- Publication No.1103., Washington, DC

USSG (1972): *The health consequences of smoking. A report of the Surgeon General: 1972.* DHEW Publication No. HSM 72-7516. Department of Health Education and Welfare, Washington, DC.

USSG (1975): *The health consequences of smoking 1975.* DHEW Publication No. CDC 76-8704. US Department of Health Education and Welfare. Public Health Service. Center for Disease Control. Atlanta, GA.

USSG (1979): *Smoking and health: A report of the Surgeon General.* DHEW publication No. (PHS):79-50066. Department of Health Education and Welfare, Washington DC.

USSG (1982): *The health consequences of smoking: Cancer. A report of the Surgeon General.* US Department of Health and Human Services. Office on Smoking and Health, Rockville, MD.

USSG (1984): *The health consequences of smoking: Chronic obstructive lung diseases. A report of the Surgeon General.* US Department of Health and Human Services, Washington, DC.

USSG (1986): *The health consequences of involuntary smoking, a report of the Surgeon General.* US Public Health Service, Rockville MD.

USSG (1989): *Reducing the health consequences of smoking: 25 years of progress. A report of the Surgeon General.* DHHS publication No. CDC 89-8411. US Department of Health and Human Services. Public Health Service. Center for Disease Control. Atlanta, GA.

USSG (1993): *The health consequences of smoking: Cardiovascular diseases. A report of the Surgeon general.* US Department of Health and Human Services, Washington, DC.

Van Loy M, et al., (1997): Dynamic behavior of semivolatile organic compounds in indoor air. Nicotine in a stainless steel chamber. *Environ Sci Technol* 31:2554-2561.

Van Duuren BL (1980): Carcinogens, cocarcinogens, and tumor inhibitors in cigarette smoke condensate. In: *A safe cigarette?* Gori GB, Bock FG, eds. pp. 105-112. Cold Spring Harbor Laboratory, Cold Spring Harbor, NY.

Wagenknecht LE, et al. (1992): Misclassification of smoking status in the CARDIA study—A comparison of self-report with serum cotinine levels. *Am J Publ Health* 82:33-36.

Wald NJ, et al. (1981): Serum cotinine levels in pipe smokers: Evidence against nicotine as a cause of coronary heart disease. *Lancet* 10: 775-777.

Wang FL, et al. (1994): Childhood and Adolescent Passive Smoking and the Risk of Female Lung Cancer. *Int J Epidemiol* 23:223-230.

Wang FL, et al. (1996): A Case-Control Study of Childhood and Adolescent Exposure to Environmental Tobacco Smoke (ETS): and the Risk of Female Lung Cancer. *Lung Cancer* 14(Suppl.1):S238.

Wang SY, et al. (1996): A Comparative Study of the Risk Factors for Lung Cancer in Guangdong, China. *Lung Cancer* 14(Suppl.1):S99-S105.

Wang TJ, et al. (1996): Lung Cancer in Nonsmoking Chinese Women: A Case-Control Study. *Lung Cancer* 14(Suppl.1):S93-S98.

Wang TJ, Zhou BS (1997): MetaAnalysis of the Potential Relationship Between Exposure to Environmental Tobacco Smoke and Lung Cancer in Nonsmoking Chinese Women. *Lung Cancer* 16:145-150.

Weed DL, Kramer BS (1997): Breast cancer studies aren't "political". *The Wall Street Journal* March 26:A19

Wu A, et al. (1985): Smoking and Other Risk Factors for Lung Cancer in Women. *J Nat Cancer Inst* 74:747-751.

Wu A, et al. (1988): Personal and Family History of Lung Disease as Risk Factors for Adenocarcitoma of the Lung. *Cancer Res* 48:7279-7284.

WuWilliams A, et al. (1990): Lung Cancer Among Women in NorthEast China. *Br Med J* 62:982-987.

Wynder EL (1987): Workshop on guidelines to the epidemiology of weak associations. *Prev Med* 16:139-141.

Wynder EL, et al. (1987): Association of Dietary Fat and Lung Cancer. *J Nat Cancer Inst* 79:631-637.

Wynder EL (1990): Epidemiological Issues in Weak Associations. *Int J Epidemiol*, 19(Suppl.1):S5-7.

Wu A, et al. (1985): Smoking and Other Risk Factors for Lung Cancer in Women. *J Nat Cancer Inst* 74:747-751.

Wu A, et al. (1988): Personal and Family History of Lung Disease as Risk Factors for Adenocarcinoma of the Lung. *Cancer Res* 48:7279-84.

Xu Z, et al. (1989): Smoking, Air Pollution, and High Rates of Lung Cancer in Shenyang, China. *J Nat Cancer Inst* 6:1800-1806.

Ye Z, et al. (1990): The Environmental Factors of Lung Cancer in Family Women. *Tianjin Chin J Clin Oncol* 17:195-198.

Yong L, et al. (1997): *Intake of Vitamins E, C, and A and Risk of Lung Cancer*: The NHANES-I Epidemiologic Followup Study, First National Health and Nutrition Examination Survey II. *Am J Epidemiol* 146:321-343.

Yu S, Zhao N (1996): Combined Analysis of Case-Control Studies of Smoking and Lung Cancer in China. *Lung Cancer* 14(Suppl.1):S161-170.

Yu ZF, et al. (1996): Environmental Factors and Lung Cancer. *Lung Cancer* 14(Suppl.1):S240-241.

Zaridze D, et al. (1994): Relation Between Exposure to Environmental Tobacco Smoke and Lung Cancer in Non-Smoking Women in Moscow. *Exper Oncol* 16:441-445.

Zhu H, Wang Z (1993): Study of Occupational Lung Cancer in Asbestos Factories in China. *Br J Ind Med*, 50:1039-1042.

Ziegler R, et al. (1986): Carotenoid Intake, Vegetables, and the Risk of Lung Cancer Among White Men in New Jersey. *Am J Epidemiol* 123:1080-1093.

DATE DUE
